With best wishes for a very Merry
Christmas to Elmer from Dorothy.

December 24, 1907.

Monsieur Beaucaire

by

Booth
Tarkington

Author of
"The Gentleman from
Indiana"

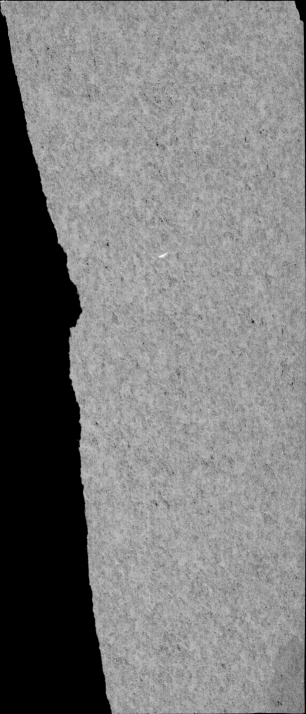

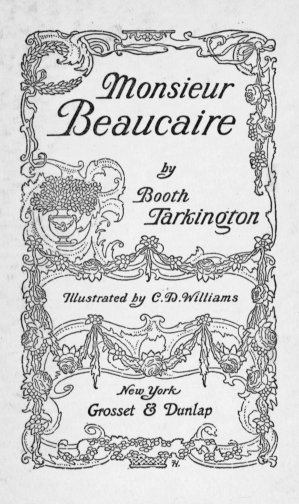

Monsieur Beaucaire

by
Booth
Tarkington

Illustrated by C. D. Williams

New York
Grosset & Dunlap

To H.T.J.

B.T.

List of
Illustrations.

The Decorations of this Book
were designed by
Chas Edw. Hooper.

Monsieur
Beaucaire

Chapter One

THE young Frenchman did very well what he had planned to do. His guess that the Duke would cheat proved good. As the unshod half-dozen figures that had been standing noiselessly in the entryway stole softly into the shadows of the chamber, he leaned across the table and smilingly plucked a card out of the big Englishman's sleeve.

"Merci, M. le Duc!" he laughed, rising and stepping back from the table.

The Englishman cried out, "It means the dirty work of silencing you with my bare hands!" and came at him.

"Do not move," said M. Beaucaire, so sharply that the other paused. "Observe behind you."

The Englishman turned, and saw what trap he had blundered into; then stood transfixed, impotent, alternately scarlet with rage and white with the vital shame of discovery. M. Beaucaire remarked, indicating the silent figures by a polite wave of the hand, "Is it not a compliment to monsieur that I procure six large men to subdue him? They are quite de-

4

vote' to me, and monsieur is alone. Could it be that he did not wish even his lackeys to know he play with the yo'ng Frenchman who Meestaire Nash does not like in the pomp-room? Monsieur is unfortunate to have come on foot and alone to my apartment."

The Duke's mouth foamed over with chaotic revilement. His captor smiled brightly, and made a slight gesture, as one who brushes aside a boisterous insect. With the same motion he quelled to stony quiet a resentful impetus of his servants toward the Englishman.

" It's murder, is it, you carrion! " finished the Duke.

M. Beaucaire lifted his shoulders in a mock shiver. " What words!

No, no, no! No killing! A such
word to a such host! No, no, not
mur-r-der; only disgrace!" He
laughed a clear, light laugh with a
rising inflection, seeming to launch
himself upon an adventurous quest for
sympathy.

"You little devilish scullion!" spat
out the Duke.

"Tut, tut! But I forget. Monsieur has pursue' his studies of deportment amongs' his fellow-country-
men."

"Do you dream a soul in Bath
will take your word that I—that
I——"

"That M. le Duc de Winterset had
a card up his sleeve?"

"You pitiful stroller, you stable-
boy, born in a stable——"

8

"Is it not an honor to be born where monsieur must have been bred?"

"You scurvy foot-boy, you greasy barber, you cutthroat groom——"

"Overwhelm'!" The young man bowed with imperturbable elation. "M. le Duc appoint' me to all the office' of his househol'."

"You mustachioed fool, there are not five people of quality in Bath will speak to you——"

"No, monsieur, not on the parade; but how many come to play with me here? Because I will play always, night or day, for what one will, for any long, and al—ways fair, monsieur."

"You outrageous varlet! Every one knows you came to England as the French Ambassador's barber.

What man of fashion will listen to
you? Who will believe you?"

"All people, monsieur. Do you
think I have not calculate', that I
shall make a failure of my little en-
terprise?"

"Bah!"

"Will monsieur not reseat himself?" M. Beaucaire made a low
bow. "So. We must not be too
tire' for Lady Malbourne's rout. Ha,
ha! And you, Jean, Victor, and you
others, retire; go in the hallway.
Attend at the entrance, François. So;
now we shall talk. Monsieur, I wish
you to think very cool. Then listen;
I will be briefly. It is that I am
well known to be all, entire' hones'.
Gamblist? Ah, yes; true and mos'
profitable; but fair, al—ways fair;

every one say that. Is it not so?
Think of it. And—is there never a
w'isper come to M. le Duc that not
all people belief him to play al—ways
hones'? Ha, ha! Did it almos' be
said to him las' year, after when he
play' with Milor' Tappin'ford at the
chocolate-house——"

"You dirty scandal-monger!" the
Duke burst out. "I'll——"

"Monsieur, monsieur!" said the
Frenchman. "It is a poor valor to
insult a helpless captor. Can he re-
tort upon his own victim? But it is
for you to think of what I say.
True, I am not reco'nize on the parade; that my frien's who come here
do not present me to their ladies;
that Meestaire Nash has reboff' me
in the pomp-room; still, am I not

11

known for being hones' and fair in
my play, and will I *not* be belief',
even I, when I lif' my voice and
charge you aloud with what is already w'isper'? Think of it! You
are a noble, and there will be some
hang-dogs who might not fall away
from you. Only such would be lef'
to you. Do you want it tol'? And
you can keep out of France, monsieur? I have lef' his service, but I
have still the ear of M. de Mirepoix,
and he know' I never lie. Not a
gentleman will play you when you
come to Paris."

The Englishman's white lip showed
a row of scarlet dots upon it. "How
much do you want?" he said.

The room rang with the gay
laughter of Beaucaire. "I hol' your

note' for seven-hunder' pound'. You
can have them, monsieur. Why does
a such great man come to play M.
Beaucaire? Because no one else will-
in' to play M. le Duc—he cannot
pay. Ha, ha! So he come' to good
Monsieur Beaucaire. Money, ha,
ha! What I want with money?"

His Grace of Winterset's features
were set awry to a sinister pattern.
He sat glaring at his companion in a
snarling silence.

"Money? Pouf!" snapped the
little gambler. "No, no, no! It is
that M. le Duc, impoverish', somewhat in a bad odor as he is, yet com-
mand the *entrée any*-where—onless
I— Ha, ha! Eh, monsieur?"

"Ha! You dare think to force
me——"

M. Beaucaire twirled the tip of his
slender mustache around the end of
his white forefinger. Then he said:
"Monsieur and me goin' to Lady
Malbourne's ball to-night—M. le Duc
and me!"

The Englishman roared, "Curse
your impudence!"

"Sit quiet. Oh, yes, that's all;
we goin' together."

"No!"

"Certain. I make all my little
plan'. 'Tis all arrange'." He paused,
and then said gravely, "You goin'
present me to Lady Mary Carlisle."

The other laughed in utter scorn.
"Lady Mary Carlisle, of all women
alive, would be the first to prefer the
devil to a man of no birth, barber."

"'Tis all arrange'; have no fear;

14

nobody question monsieur's guest. You goin' take me to-night——"

"No!"

"Yes. And after—then *I* have the *entrée*. Is it much I ask? This one little favor, and I never w'isper, never breathe that—it is to say, I am always forever silent of monsieur's misfortune."

"*You* have the *entrée!*" sneered the other. "Go to a lackeys' rout and dance with the kitchen maids. If I would, I could not present you to Bath society. I should have cartels from the fathers, brothers, and lovers of every wench and madam in the place, even I. You would be thrust from Lady Malbourne's door five minutes after you entered it."

"No, no, no!"

15

" Half the gentlemen in Bath have been here to play. They would know you, wouldn't they, fool? You've had thousands out of Bantison, Rakell, Guilford, and Townbrake. They would have you lashed by the grooms as your ugly deserts are. *You* to speak to Lady Mary Carlisle! 'Od's blood! You! Also, dolt, she would know you if you escaped the others. She stood within a yard of you when Nash expelled you the pump-room."

M. Beaucaire flushed slightly. "You think I did not see?" he asked.

"Do you dream that because Winterset introduces a low fellow he will be tolerated—that Bath will receive a barber?"

16

"I have the distinction to call monsieur's attention," replied the young man gayly, "I have renounce' that profession."

"Fool!"

"I am now a man of honor!"

"Faugh!"

"A man of the parts," continued the young Frenchman, "and of deportment; is it not so? Have you seen me of a fluster, or gross ever, or, what shall I say—*bourgeois?* Shall you be shame' for your guest' manner? No, no! And my appearance, is it of the people? Clearly, no. Do I not compare in taste of apparel with your yo'ng Englishman? Ha, ha! To be hope'. Ha, ha! So I am goin' talk with Lady Mary Carlisle."

"Bah!" The Duke made a savage burlesque. "'Lady Mary Carlisle, may I assume the honor of presenting the barber of the Marquis de Mirepoix?' So, is it?"

"No, monsieur," smiled the young man. "Quite not so. You shall have nothing to worry you, nothing in the worl'. I am goin' to assassinate my poor mustachio—also remove this horrible black peruke, and emerge in my own hair. Behol'!" He swept the heavy, curled mass from his head as he spoke, and his hair, coiled under the great wig, fell to his shoulders, and sparkled yellow in the candle-light. He tossed his head to shake the hair back from his cheeks. "When it is dress', I am transform'; nobody can know me; you shall ob-

serve. See how little I ask of you,
how very little bit. No one shall rec-
o'nize 'M. Beaucaire' or 'Victor.'
Ha, ha! 'Tis all arrange'; you have
nothing to fear."

"Curse you," said the Duke, "do
you think I'm going to be saddled
with you wherever I go as long as
you choose?"

"A mistake. No. All I requi—
All I beg—is this one evening. 'Tis
all shall be necessary. *After*, I shall
not need monsieur."

"Take heed to yourself—after!"
vouchsafed the Englishman between
his teeth.

"Conquered!" cried M. Beau-
caire, and clapped his hands gleefully.
"Conquered for the night! Aha, it
is riz'nable! I shall meet what you

send—after. One cannot hope too much of your patience. It is but natural you should attemp' a little avengement for the rascal trap I was such a wicked fellow as to set for you. I shall meet some strange frien's of yours after to-night; not so? I must try to be not too much frighten'." He looked at the Duke curiously. "You want to know why I create this tragedy, why I am so unkind as to entrap monsieur?"

His Grace of Winterset replied with a chill glance; a pulse in the nobleman's cheek beat less relentlessly; his eye raged not so bitterly; the steady purple of his own color was returning; his voice was less hoarse; he was regaining his habit. "'Tis ever the manner of the vulgar," he observed, "to wish to be seen with people of fashion."

"Oh, no, no, no!" The Frenchman laughed. "'Tis not that. Am I not already one of these 'men of fashion'? I lack only the reputation of birth. Monsieur is goin' supply that. Ha, ha! I shall be noble from to-night. 'Victor,' the artis', is condemn' to death; his throat shall be cut with his own razor. 'M. Beaucaire'—" Here the young man sprang to his feet, caught up the black wig, clapped into it a dice-box from the table, and hurled it violently through the open door. "'M. Beaucaire' shall be choke' with his own dice-box. Who is the Phœnix to remain? What advantage have I not over other men of rank who are merely born to it? I may choose my own. No! Choose for me, monsieur. Shall I be chevalier, comte, vicomte, marquis, what? None. Out of compliment to monsieur can I wish to be anything he is not? No, no! I shall be M. le Duc, M. le Duc de—de Chateaurien. Ha, ha! You see? You are my *confrère.*"

M. Beaucaire trod a dainty step or two, waving his hand politely to the Duke, as though in invitation to join the celebration of his rank. The Englishman watched, his eye still and harsh, already gathering in craftiness. Beaucaire stopped suddenly. "But how I forget my age! I am twenty-three," he said, with a sigh. "I rejoice too much to be of the quality. It has been too great for me, and I had always belief' myself free of such ambition. I thought it was enough to behol' the opera without wishing to sing; but no, England have teach' me I have those vulgar desire'. Monsieur, I am goin' tell you a secret; the ladies of your country are very diff'runt than ours. One may adore the demoiselle, one must worship the lady of England. Our ladies have the —it is the beauty of youth; yours remain comely at thirty. Ours are flowers, yours are stars! See, I betray myself, I am so poor a patriot. And there is one among these stars— ah, yes, there is one—the poor Frenchman has observe' from his humble distance; even there he could bask in the glowing!" M. Beaucaire turned to the window, and looked out into

the dark. He did not see the lights
of the town. When he turned again,
he had half forgotten his prisoner;
other pictures were before him.

"Ah, what radiance!" he cried.
"Those people up over the sky, they
want to show they wish the earth to
be happy, so they smile, and make
this lady. Gold-haired, an angel of
heaven, and yet a Diana of the chase!
I see her fly by me on her great
horse one day; she touch' his mane
with her fingers. I buy that clipping
from the groom. I have it here with
my dear brother's picture. Ah, *you!*
Oh, yes, you laugh! What do you
know! 'Twas all I could get. But
I have heard of the endeavor of M.
le Duc to recoup his fortunes. This
alliance shall fail. It is not the way

26

—that heritage shall be safe' from him! It is you and me, monsieur! You can laugh! The war is open', and by *me!* There is one great step taken : until to-night there was nothing for you to ruin, to-morrow you have got a noble of France—your own *protégé*—to besiege and sack. And you are to lose, because you think such ruin easy, and because you understand nothing—far less—of divinity. How could you know? You have not the fiber; the heart of a lady is a blank to you; you know nothing of the vibration. There are some words that were made only to tell of Lady Mary, for her alone— *bellissima*, divine, *glorieuse!* Ah, how I have watch' her! It is sad to me when I see her surround' by your

27

yo'ng captains, your nobles, your rat-
tles, your beaux—ha, ha!—and I
mus' hol' far aloof. It is sad for me
—but oh, jus' to watch her and to
wonder! Strange it is, but I have almos' cry out with rapture at a look I
have see' her give another man, so
beautiful it was, so tender, so dazzling
of the eyes and so mirthful of the
lips. Ah, divine coquetry! A look
for another, *ah-i-me!* for many others; and even to you, one day, a rose,
while I—I, monsieur, could not even
be so blessed as to be the groun' beneath her little shoe! But *to-night*,
monsieur—ha, ha!—*to-night*, monsieur, you and me, two princes, M. le
Duc de Winterset and M. le Duc de
Chateaurien—ha, ha! you see?—we
are goin' arm-in-arm to that ball, and

I am goin' have one of those looks, *I!* And a rose! *I!* It is time. But ten minute', monsieur. I make my apology to keep you waitin' so long while I go in the nex' room and execute my poor mustachio—that will be my only murder for jus' this one evening—and inves' myself in white satin. Ha, ha! I shall be very gran', monsieur. François, send Louis to me; Victor, to order two chairs for monsieur and me; we are goin' out in the worl' to-night!"

Chapter
Two

HE chairmen swarmed
in the street at Lady
Malbourne's door,
where the joyous vul-
gar fought with mud-
dled footmen and tipsy link-boys for
places of vantage whence to catch
a glimpse of quality and of raiment
at its utmost.　Dawn was in the east,
and the guests were departing. Singly
or in pairs, glittering in finery, they
came mincing down the steps, the

ghost of the night's smirk fading to jadedness as they sought the dark recesses of their chairs. From within sounded the twang of fiddles still swinging manfully at it, and the windows were bright with the light of many candles. When the door was flung open to call the chair of Lady Mary Carlisle, there was an eager pressure of the throng to see.

A small, fair gentleman in white satin came out upon the steps, turned and bowed before a lady who appeared in the doorway, a lady whose royal loveliness was given to view for a moment in that glowing frame. The crowd sent up a hearty English cheer for the Beauty of Bath.

The gentleman smiled upon them delightedly. "What enchanting people!" he cried. "Why did I not know, so I might have shout' with them?" The lady noticed the people not at all; whereat, being pleased, the people cheered again. The gentleman offered her his hand; she made a slow courtesy; placed the tips of her fingers upon his own. "I am honored, M. de Chateaurien," she said.

"No, no!" he cried earnestly. "Behol' a poor Frenchman whom emperors should envy." Then reverently and with the pride of his gallant office vibrant in every line of his light figure, invested in white satin and very grand, as he had prophesied, M. le Duc de Chateaurien handed Lady Mary Carlisle down the steps, an achievement which had figured in

the ambitions of seven other gentlemen during the evening.

"Am I to be lef' in such on-
happiness?" he said in a low voice.
"That rose I have beg' for so
long——"

"Never!" said Lady Mary.

"Ah, I do not deserve it, I know
so well! But——"

"Never!"

"It is the greatness of my on-
worthiness that alone can claim your
charity; let your kin' heart give this
little red rose, this great alms, to the
poor beggar."

"Never!"

She was seated in the chair. "Ah,
give the rose," he whispered. Her
beauty shone dazzlingly on him out of
the dimness.

" Never ! " she flashed defiantly as she was closed in. " Never ! "

" Ah ! "

" Never ! "

The rose fell at his feet.

" A rose lasts till morning," said a voice behind him.

Turning, M. de Chateaurien looked beamingly upon the face of the Duke of Winterset.

" 'Tis already the daylight," he replied, pointing to the east. " Monsieur, was it not enough honor for you to han' out madame, the aunt of Lady Mary? Lady Rellerton retain' much trace of beauty. 'Tis strange you did not appear more happy."

" The rose is of an unlucky color, I think," observed the Duke.

"The color of a blush, my brother."

"Unlucky, I still maintain," said the other calmly.

"The color of the veins of a Frenchman. Ha, ha!" cried the young man. "What price would be too high? A rose is a rose! A good-night, my brother, a good-night. I wish you dreams of roses, red roses, only beautiful red, red roses!"

"Stay! Did you see the look she gave these street folk when they shouted for her? And how are you higher than they, when she knows? As high as yonder horse-boy!"

"Red roses, my brother, only roses. I wish you dreams of red, red roses!"

Chapter Three

'T WAS well agreed by
the fashion of Bath
that M. le Duc de
Chateaurien was a per-
son of sensibility and
haut ton; that his retinue and equipage
surpassed in elegance; that his person
was exquisite, his manner engaging.
In the company of gentlemen his
ease was slightly tinged with gra-
ciousness (his single equal in Bath being his Grace of Winterset); but it

was remarked that when he bowed
over a lady's hand, his air bespoke
only a gay and tender reverence.

He was the idol of the dowagers
within a week after his appearance;
matrons warmed to him ; young belles
looked sweetly on him, while the
gentlemen were won to admiration or envy. He was of prodi-
gious wealth : old Mr. Bicksit, who
dared not, for his fame's sake, fail to
have seen all things, had visited Chateaurien under the present Duke's
father, and descanted to the curious
upon its grandeurs. The young noble
had one fault, he was so poor a gambler. He cared nothing for the haz-
ards of a die or the turn of a card.
Gayly admitting that he had been
born with no spirit of adventure in

him, he was sure, he declared, that he failed of much happiness by his lack of taste in such matters.

But he was not long wanting the occasion to prove his taste in the matter of handling a weapon. A certain led-captain, Rohrer by name, notorious, amongst other things, for bearing a dexterous and bloodthirsty blade, came to Bath post-haste, one night, and jostled heartily against him in the pump-room on the following morning. M. de Chateaurien bowed, and turned aside without offense, continuing a conversation with some gentlemen near by. Captain Rohrer jostled against him a second time. M. de Chateaurien looked him in the eye, and apologized pleasantly for being so much in the way. Thereupon

38

Rohrer procured an introduction to
him, and made some observations de-
rogatory to the valor and virtue of
the French.

There was current a curious piece
of gossip of the French court: a
prince of the blood royal, grandson
of the late Regent and second in the
line of succession to the throne of
France, had rebelled against the au-
thority of Louis XV., who had commanded him to marry the Princess
Henriette, cousin to both of them.
The princess was reported to be
openly devoted to the cousin who re-
fused to accept her hand at the bid-
ding of the king; and, as rumor ran,
the prince's caprice elected in prefer-
ence the discipline of Vincennes, to
which retirement the furious king

had consigned him. The story was the staple gossip of all polite Europe; and Captain Rohrer, having in his mind a purpose to make use of it in leading up to a statement that should be general to the damage of all Frenchwomen, and which a Frenchman might not pass over as he might a jog of the elbow, repeated it with garbled truths to make a scandal of a story which bore none on a plain relation.

He did not reach his deduction. M. de Chateaurien, breaking into his narrative, addressed him very quietly. "Monsieur," he said, "none but swine deny the nobleness of that good and gentle lady, Mademoiselle la Princesse de Bourbon-Conti. Every Frenchman know' that her cousin is a bad rebel and ingrate, who had only honor and rispec' for her, but was so wilful he could not let even the king say, 'You shall marry here, you shall marry there.' My frien's," the young man turned to the others, "may I ask you to close roun' in a circle for one moment? It is clearly shown that the Duke of Orleans is a scurvy fellow, but not—" he wheeled about and touched Captain Rohrer on the brow with the back of his gloved hand—"but not so scurvy as thou, thou swine of the gutter!"

Two hours later, with perfect ease, he ran Captain Rohrer through the left shoulder—after which he sent a basket of red roses to the Duke of Winterset. In a few days he had another captain to fight. This was a

ruffling buck who had the astounding
indiscretion to proclaim M. de Chateaurien an impostor. There was no
Chateaurien, he swore. The Frenchman laughed in his face, and, at twi-
light of the same day, pinked him
carefully through the right shoulder.
It was not that he could not put aside
the insult to himself, he declared to
Mr. Molyneux, his second, and the
few witnesses, as he handed his wet
sword to his lackey—one of his station could not be insulted by a doubt
of that station—but he fought in the
quarrel of his friend Winterset. This
rascal had asserted that M. le Duc
had introduced an impostor. Could
he overlook the insult to a friend, one
to whom he owed his kind recep-
tion in Bath? Then, bending over

his fallen adversary, he whispered:
" Naughty man, tell your master find
some better quarrel for the nex' he
sen' agains' me."

The conduct of M. de Chateaurien
was pronounced admirable.

There was no surprise when the
young foreigner fell naturally into the
long train of followers of the beautiful Lady Mary Carlisle, nor was there
great astonishment that he should ob-
tain marked favor in her eyes, shown
so plainly that my Lord Townbrake,
Sir Hugh Guilford, and the rich
Squire Bantison, all of whom had followed her through three seasons, swore
with rage, and his Grace of Winterset stalked from her aunt's house with
black brows.

Meeting the Duke there on the

evening after his second encounter,
de Chateaurien smiled upon him brilliantly. " It was badly done ; *oh,* so
badly ! " he whispered. " Can you
afford to have me strip' of my mask
by any but yourself ? You, who introduce' me ? They will say there is
some bad scandal that I could force
you to be my god-father. You mus'
get the courage yourself."

" I told you a rose had a short
life," was the answer.

" Oh, those roses ! 'Tis the very
greates' rizzon to gather each day a
fresh one." He took a red bud from
his breast for an instant, and touched
it to his lips.

"M. de Chateaurien ! " It was
Lady Mary's voice ; she stood at a
table where a vacant place had been

left beside her. "M. de Chateaurien, we have been waiting very long for you."

The Duke saw the look she did not know she gave the Frenchman, and he lost countenance for a moment.

"We approach a climax, eh, monsieur?" said M. de Chateaurien.

Chapter
Four

THERE fell a clear September night, when the moon was radiant over town and country, over cobbled streets and winding roads. From the fields the mists rose slowly, and the air was mild and fragrant, while distances were white and full of mystery. All of Bath that pretended to fashion or condition was present that evening at a *fête* at the house of a

country gentleman of the neighbor-
hood. When the stately junket was
concluded, it was the pleasure of M.
de Chateaurien to form one of the
escort of Lady Mary's carriage for the
return. As they took the road, Sir
Hugh Guilford and Mr. Bantison, engaging in indistinct but vigorous re-
monstrance with Mr. Molyneux over
some matter, fell fifty or more paces
behind, where they continued to ride,
keeping up their argument. Half a
dozen other gallants rode in advance,
muttering among themselves, or at-
tended laxly upon Lady Mary's aunt
on the other side of the coach, while
the happy Frenchman was permitted
to ride close to that adorable window
which framed the fairest face in England.

He sang for her a little French song, a song of the *voyageur* who dreamed of home. The lady, listening, looking up at the bright moon, felt a warm drop upon her cheek, and he saw the tears sparkling upon her lashes.

"Mademoiselle," he whispered then, "I, too, have been a wanderer, but my dreams were not of France; no, I do not dream of that home, of that dear country. It is of a dearer country, a dream country—a country of gold and snow," he cried softly, looking at her white brow and the fair, lightly powdered hair above it. "Gold and snow, and the blue sky of a lady's eyes!"

"I had thought the ladies of France were dark, sir."

"Cruel! It is that she will not understan'! Have I speak of the ladies of France? No, no, no! It is of the faires' country; yes, 'tis a province of heaven, mademoiselle. Do I not renounce my allegiance to France? Oh, yes! I am subjec'— no, content to be slave—in the lan' of the blue sky, the gold, and the snow."

"A very pretty figure," answered Lady Mary, her eyes downcast. "But does it not hint a notable experience in the making of such speeches?"

"Tormentress! No. It prove' only the inspiration it is to know you."

"We English ladies hear plenty of the like, sir; and we even grow brilliant enough to detect the assurance that lies beneath the courtesies of our own gallants."

"*Merci!* I should believe so!" ejaculated M. de Chateaurien; but he smothered the words upon his lips.

Her eyes were not lifted. She went on: "We come, in time, to believe that true feeling comes faltering forth, not glibly; that smoothness betokens the adept in the art, sir, rather than your true—your true—" She was herself faltering; more, blushing deeply, and halting to a full stop in terror of a word. There was a silence.

"Your—true—lover," he said huskily. When he had said that word both trembled. She turned half away into the darkness of the coach.

"I know what make' you to doubt

me," he said, faltering himself, though
it was not his art that prompted him.
"They have tol' you the French do
nothing al—ways but make love, is it
not so? Yes, you think *I* am like
that. You think I am like that
now!"

She made no sign.

"I suppose," he sighed, "I am un-
riz'nable; I would have the snow not
so col'—for jus' me."

She did not answer.

"Turn to me," he said.

The fragrance of the fields came to
them, and from the distance the faint,
clear note of a hunting-horn.

"Turn to me."

The lovely head was bent very low.
Her little gloved hand lay upon the
narrow window ledge. He laid his

own gently upon it. The two hands were shaking like twin leaves in the breeze. Hers was not drawn away. After a pause, neither knew how long, he felt the warm fingers turn and clasp themselves tremulously about his own. At last she looked up bravely and met his eyes. The horn was wound again—nearer.

"All the cold was gone from the snows—long ago," she said.

"My beautiful!" he whispered; it was all he could say. "My beautiful!" But she clutched his arm, startled.

"*'Ware the road!*" A wild halloo sounded ahead. The horn wound loudly. "*'Ware the road!*" There sprang up out of the night a flying thunder of hoof-beats. The gentlemen riding idly in front of the coach scattered to the hedge-sides; and, with drawn swords flashing in the moon, a party of horsemen charged down the highway, their cries blasting the night.

"Barber! Kill the barber!" they screamed. "Barber! Kill the barber!"

Beaucaire had but time to draw his sword when they were upon him.

"*À moi!*" his voice rang out clearly as he rose in his stirrups. "*À moi*, François, Louis, Berquin! *À moi*, François!"

The cavaliers came straight at him. He parried the thrust of the first, but the shock of collision hurled his horse against the side of the coach.

"Sacred swine!" he cried bitterly. "To endanger a lady, to make this brawl in a lady's presence! Drive on!" he shouted.

"No!" cried Lady Mary.

The Frenchman's assailants were masked, but they were not highwaymen. "Barber! Barber!" they shouted hoarsely, and closed in on him in a circle.

"See how he use his steel!" laughed M. Beaucaire, as his point passed through a tawdry waistcoat. For a moment he cut through the ring and cleared a space about him, and Lady Mary saw his face shining in the moonlight. "*Canaille!*" he hissed, as his horse sank beneath him; and, though guarding his head from the rain of blows from above, he managed to drag headlong from his saddle the man who had hamstrung the poor brute. The fellow came suddenly to the ground, and lay there.

"Is it not a compliment," said a heavy voice, " to bring six large men to subdue monsieur ? "

"Oh, you are there, my frien' ! In the rear—a little in the rear, I think. Ha, ha ! "

The Frenchman's play with his weapon was a revelation of skill, the more extraordinary as he held in his hand only a light dress sword. But the ring closed about him, and his keen defense could not avail him for more than a few moments. Lady Mary's outriders, the gallants of her escort, rode up close to the coach and encircled it, not interfering.

"Sir Hugh Guilford!" cried Lady Mary wildly, "if you will not help him, give me your sword!" She would have leaped to the ground, but Sir Hugh held the door.

"Sit quiet, madam," he said to her; then, to the man on the box, "Drive on."

"If he does, I'll kill him!" she said fiercely. "Ah, what cowards! Will you see the Duke murdered?"

"The Duke!" laughed Guilford. "They will not kill him, unless—be easy, dear madam, 'twill be explained. Gad's life!" he muttered to Molyneux, "'Twere time the varlet had his lashing! D'ye hear her?"

"Barber or no barber," answered Molyneux, "I wish I had warned him. He fights as few gentlemen could. Ah—ah! Look at that! 'Tis a shame!"

On foot, his hat gone, his white coat sadly rent and gashed, flecked, too, with red, M. Beaucaire, wary, alert, brilliant, seemed to transform himself into a dozen fencing-masters; and, though his skill appeared to lie in delicacy and quickness, his play being continually with the point, sheer strength failed to beat him down. The young man was laughing like a child.

"Believe me," said Molyneux, "he's no barber! No, and never was!"

For a moment there was even a chance that M. Beaucaire might have the best of it. Two of his adversaries were prostrate, more than one were groaning, and the indomitable Frenchman had actually almost beat off the ruffians, when, by a trick, he was overcome. One of them, dismounting, ran in suddenly from behind, and seized his blade in a thick leather gauntlet. Before Beaucaire could disengage the weapon, two others threw themselves from their horses and hurled him to the earth. "*À moi! À moi*, François!" he cried as he went down, his sword in fragments, but his voice unbroken and clear.

"Shame!" muttered one or two of the gentlemen about the coach.

"'Twas dastardly to take him so," said Molyneux. "Whatever his deservings, I'm nigh of a mind to offer him a rescue in the Duke's face."

"Truss him up, lads," said the

heavy voice. " Clear the way in front of the coach. There sit those whom we avenge upon a presumptuous lackey. Now, Whiffen, you have a fair audience, lay on and baste him."

Two men began to drag M. Beaucaire toward a great oak by the roadside. Another took from his saddle a heavy whip with three thongs.

" *À moi, François!* "

There was borne on the breeze an answer—" *Monseigneur! Monseigneur!* " The cry grew louder suddenly. The clatter of hoofs urged to an anguish of speed sounded on the night. M. Beaucaire's servants had lagged sorely behind, but they made up for it now. Almost before the noise of their own steeds they came riding down the moonlit aisle be-

tween the mists. Chosen men, these
servants of Beaucaire, and like a
thunderbolt they fell upon the astounded cavaliers.

"Chateaurien! Chateaurien!" they
shouted, and smote so swiftly that,
through lack of time, they showed
no proper judgment, discriminating
nothing between non-combatants and
their master's foes. They charged
first into the group about M. Beaucaire, and broke and routed it utterly.
Two of them leaped to the young
man's side, while the other four,
swerving, scarce losing the momen-
tum of their onset, bore on upon the
gentlemen near the coach, who went
down beneath the fierceness of the
onslaught, cursing manfully.

"Our just deserts," said Mr. Molyneux, his mouth full of dust and philosophy.

Sir Hugh Guilford's horse fell with him, being literally ridden over, and the baronet's leg was pinned under the saddle. In less than ten minutes from the first attack on M. Beaucaire, the attacking party had fled in disorder, and the patrician non-combatants, choking with expletives, consumed with wrath, were prisoners, disarmed by the Frenchman's lackeys.

Guilford's discomfiture had freed the doors of the coach ; so it was that when M. Beaucaire, struggling to rise, assisted by his servants, threw out one hand to balance himself, he found it seized between two small, cold palms, and he looked into two warm, dilating eyes, that were doubly beautiful because of the fright and rage that found room in them, too.

M. le Duc Chateaurien sprang to his feet without the aid of his lackeys, and bowed low before Lady Mary.

"I make ten thousan' apology to be the cause of a such *mêlée* in your presence," he said; and then, turning to François, he spoke in French: "Ah, thou scoundrel! A little, and it had been too late."

François knelt in the dust before him. "Pardon!" he said. "Monseigneur commanded us to follow far in the rear, to remain unobserved. The wind malignantly blew against monseigneur's voice."

"See what it might have cost, my children," said his master, pointing to the ropes with which they would have bound him and to the whip lying beside them. A shudder passed over the lackey's frame; the utter horror in his face echoed in the eyes of his fellows.

"Oh, monseigneur!" François sprang back, and tossed his arms to heaven.

"But it did not happen," said M. Beaucaire.

"It could not!" exclaimed François.

"No. And you did very well, my children—" the young man smiled benevolently—"very well. And now," he continued, turning to Lady Mary and speaking in English, "let me be asking of our gallants yonder what make' them to be in cabal with highwaymen. One should come to a polite understanding with them, you think ? Not so ?"

He bowed, offering his hand to conduct her to the coach, where Molyneux and his companions, having drawn Sir Hugh from under his horse, were engaged in reviving and reassuring Lady Rellerton, who had fainted. But Lady Mary stayed Beaucaire with a gesture, and the two stood where they were.

"Monseigneur!" she said, with a note of raillery in her voice, but raillery so tender that he started with happiness. His movement brought him a hot spasm of pain, and he clapped his hand to a red stain on his waistcoat.

"You are hurt!"

"It is nothing," smiled M. Beaucaire. Then, that she might not see the stain spreading, he held his handkerchief over the spot. "I am a little—but jus' a trifling—bruise'; 'tis all."

"You shall ride in the coach," she whispered. "Will you be pleased, M. de Chateaurien?"

"Ah, my beautiful!" She seemed to wave before him like a shining mist. "I wish that ride might las' for al—ways! Can you say that, mademoiselle?"

"Monseigneur," she cried in a passion of admiration, "I would what you would have be, should be. What do you not deserve? You are the bravest man in the world!"

"Ha, ha! I am jus' a poor Frenchman."

"Would that a few Englishmen had shown themselves as 'poor' to-night. The vile cowards, not to help you!" With that, suddenly possessed by her anger, she swept away from him to the coach.

Sir Hugh, groaning loudly, was being assisted into the vehicle.

"My little poltroons," she said, "what are you doing with your fellow-craven, Sir Hugh Guilford, there?"

"Madam," replied Molyneux humbly, "Sir Hugh's leg is broken. Lady Rellerton graciously permits him to be taken in."

"*I* do not permit it! M. de Chateaurien rides with us."

"But——"

"Sir! Leave the wretch to groan

by the roadside," she cried fiercely, "which plight I would were that of all of you! But there will be a pretty story for the gossips to-morrow! And I could almost find pity for you when I think of the wits when you return to town. Fine gentlemen you; hardy bravoes, by heaven! to leave one man to meet a troop of horse single-handed, while you huddle in shelter until you are overthrown and disarmed by servants! Oh, the wits! Heaven save you from the wits!"

"Madam."

"Address me no more! M. de Chateaurien, Lady Rellerton and I will greatly esteem the honor of your company. Will you come?"

She stepped quickly into the coach, and was gathering her skirts to make room for the Frenchman, when a heavy voice spoke from the shadows of the tree by the wayside.

"Lady Mary Carlisle will, no doubt, listen to a word of counsel on this point."

The Duke of Winterset rode out into the moonlight, composedly untieing a mask from about his head. He had not shared the flight of his followers, but had retired into the shade of the oak, whence he now made his presence known with the utmost coolness.

"Gracious heavens, 'tis Winterset!" exclaimed Lady Rellerton.

"Turned highwayman and cutthroat," cried Lady Mary.

"No, no," laughed M. Beaucaire, somewhat unsteadily, as he stood, swaying a little, with one hand on the coach-door, the other pressed hard on his side, " he only oversee' ; he is jus' a little bashful, sometime'. He is a great man, but he don' want *all* the glory ! ''

" Barber," replied the Duke, " I must tell you that I gladly descend to bandy words with you ; your monstrous impudence is a claim to rank I cannot ignore. But a lackey who has himself followed by six other lackeys——''

" Ha, ha ! Has not M. le Duc been busy all this evening to justify me ? And I think mine mus' be the bes' six. Ha, ha ! You think ? ''

" M. de Chateaurien," said Lady Mary, " we are waiting for you."

" Pardon," he replied. " He has

something to say; maybe it is bes' if you hear it now."

" I wish to hear nothing from him —ever ! "

" My faith, madam," cried the Duke, " this saucy fellow has paid you the last insult ! He is so sure of you he does not fear you will believe the truth. When all is told, if you do not agree he deserved the lashing we planned to——"

" I'll hear no more ! "

" You will bitterly repent it, madam. For your own sake I entreat——"

" And I also," broke in M. Beaucaire. " Permit me, mademoiselle ; let him speak."

" Then let him be brief," said Lady Mary, " for I am earnest to be quit of him. His explanation of an attack on my friend and on my carriage should be made to my brother."

"Alas that he was not here," said the Duke, "to aid me! Madam, was your carriage threatened? I have endeavored only to expunge a debt I owed to Bath and to avenge an insult offered to yourself through——"

"Sir, sir, my patience will bear little more!"

"A thousan' apology," said M. Beaucaire. "You will listen, I only beg, Lady Mary?"

She made an angry gesture of assent.

"Madam, I will be brief as I may. Two months ago there came to Bath a French gambler calling himself

Beaucaire, a desperate fellow with
the cards or dice, and all the men of
fashion went to play at his lodging,
where he won considerable sums.
He was small, wore a black wig and
mustachio. He had the insolence to
show himself everywhere until the
Master of Ceremonies rebuffed him
in the pump-room, as you know, and
after that he forbore his visits to the
rooms. Mr. Nash explained (and
was confirmed, madam, by indubit-
able information) that this Beaucaire
was a man of unspeakable, vile, low
birth, being, in fact, no other than a
lackey of the French king's ambassador, Victor by name, de Mirepoix's
barber. Although his condition was
known, the hideous impudence of
the fellow did not desert him, and he

remained in Bath, where none would speak to him."

"Is your farrago nigh done, sir?"

"A few moments, madam. One evening, three weeks gone, I observed a very elegant equipage draw up to my door, and the Duke of Chateaurien was announced. The young man's manners were worthy—according to the French acceptance—and 'twere idle to deny him the most monstrous assurance. He declared himself a noble traveling for pleasure. He had taken lodgings in Bath for a season, he said, and called at once to pay his respects to me. His tone was so candid—in truth, I am the simplest of men, very easily gulled—and his stroke so bold, that I did not for one moment suspect him;

and, to my poignant regret—though in the humblest spirit I have shown myself eager to atone—that very evening I had the shame of presenting him to yourself."

" The shame, sir ! "

" Have patience, pray, madam. Ay, the shame ! You know what figure he hath cut in Bath since that evening. All ran merrily with him until several days ago Captain Badger denounced him as an impostor, vowing that Chateaurien was nothing."

" Pardon," interrupted M. Beaucaire. " ' Castle Nowhere ' would have been so much better. Why did you not make him say it that way, monsieur ? "

Lady Mary started ; she was looking at the Duke, and her face was white. He continued : " Poor Captain Badger was stabbed that same day——"

" Most befitting poor Captain Badger," muttered Molyneux.

" —And his adversary had the marvelous insolence to declare that he fought in *my* quarrel ! This afternoon the wounded man sent for me, and imparted a very horrifying intelligence. He had discovered a lackey whom he had seen waiting upon Beaucaire in attendance at the door of this Chateaurien's lodging. Beaucaire had disappeared the day before Chateaurien's arrival. Captain Badger looked closely at Chateaurien at their next meeting, and identified him with the missing Beaucaire beyond the faintest doubt. Overcome

77

with indignation, he immediately proclaimed the impostor. Out of regard for me, he did not charge him with being Beaucaire; the poor soul was unwilling to put upon me the humiliation of having introduced a barber; but the secret weighed upon him till he sent for me and put everything in my hands. I accepted the odium; thinking only of atonement. I went to Sir John Wimpledon's *fête*. I took poor Sir Hugh, there, and these other gentlemen aside, and told them my news. We narrowly observed this man, and were shocked at our simplicity in not having discovered him before. These are men of honor and cool judgment, madam. Mr. Molyneux had acted for him in the affair of Captain

Badger, and was strongly prejudiced in his favor; but Mr. Molyneux, Sir Hugh, Mr. Bantison, every one of them, in short, recognized him. In spite of his smooth face and his light hair, the adventurer Beaucaire was writ upon him amazing plain. Look at him, madam, if he will dare the inspection. You saw this Beaucaire well, the day of his expulsion from the rooms. Is not this he?"

M. Beaucaire stepped close to her. Her pale face twitched.

"Look!" he said.

"Oh, oh!" she whispered with a dry throat, and fell back in the carriage.

"Is it so?" cried the Duke.

"I do not know.—I—cannot tell."

"One moment more. I begged

these gentlemen to allow me to wipe out the insult I had unhappily offered to Bath, but particularly to you. They agreed not to forestall me or to interfere. I left Sir John Wimpledon's early, and arranged to give the sorry rascal a lashing under your own eyes, a satisfaction due the lady into whose presence he had dared to force himself."

"'*Noblesse oblige*'?" said M. Beaucaire in a tone of gentle inquiry.

"And now, madam," said the Duke, "I will detain you not one second longer. I plead the good purpose of my intentions, begging you to believe that the desire to avenge a hateful outrage, next to the wish to serve you, forms the dearest motive in the heart of Winterset."

"Bravo!" cried Beaucaire softly.

Lady Mary leaned toward him, a thriving terror in her eyes. "It is false?" she faltered.

"Monsieur should not have been born so high. He could have made little book'."

"You mean it is false?" she cried breathlessly.

"'Od's blood, is she not convinced?" broke out Mr. Bantison. "Fellow, were you not the ambassador's barber?"

"It is all false?" she whispered.

"The mos' fine art, mademoiselle. How long you think it take M. de Winterset to learn that speech after he write it out? It is a mix of what is true and the mos' chaste art. Monsieur has become a man of letters.

Perhaps he may enjoy that more than the wars. Ha, ha!"

Mr. Bantison burst into a roar of laughter. "Do French gentlemen fight lackeys? Ho, ho, ho! A pretty country! We English do as was done to-night, have our servants beat them."

"And attend ourselves," added M. Beaucaire, looking at the Duke, "somewhat in the background? But, pardon," he mocked, "that remind' me. François, return to Mr. Bantison and these gentlemen their weapons."

"Will you answer a question?" said Molyneux mildly.

"Oh, with pleasure, monsieur."

"Were you ever a barber?"

"No, monsieur," laughed the young man.

"Pah!" exclaimed Bantison. "Let me question him. Now, fellow, a confession may save you from jail. Do you deny you are Beaucaire?"

"Deny to a such judge?"

"Ha!" said Bantison. "What more do you want, Molyneux? Fellow, do you deny that you came to London in the ambassador's suite?"

"No, I do not deny."

"He admits it! Didn't you come as his barber?"

"Yes, my frien', as his barber."

Lady Mary cried out faintly, and, shuddering, put both hands over her eyes.

"I'm sorry," said Molyneux. "You fight like a gentleman."

"I thank you, monsieur."

"You called yourself Beaucaire?"

"Yes, monsieur." He was swaying to and fro; his servants ran to
support him.

"I wish——" continued Molyneux,
hesitating. "Evil take me!—but I'm
sorry you're hurt."

"Assist Sir Hugh into my carriage," said Lady Mary.

"Farewell, mademoiselle!" M.
Beaucaire's voice was very faint. His
eyes were fixed upon her face. She
did not look toward him.

They were propping Sir Hugh on
the cushions. The Duke rode up
close to Beaucaire, but François seized
his bridle fiercely, and forced the
horse back on its haunches.

"The man's servants worship him"
said Molyneux.

"Curse your insolence!" exclaimed the Duke. "How much am I to bear from this varlet and his varlets? Beaucaire, if you have not left Bath by to-morrow noon, you will be clapped into jail, and the lashing you escaped to-night shall be given you thrice tenfold!"

"I shall be—in the—Assembly— Room' at nine—o'clock, one week —from—to-night," answered the young man, smiling jauntily, though his lips were colorless. The words cost him nearly all his breath and strength. "You mus' keep—in the —backgroun', monsieur. Ha, ha!"

The door of the coach closed with a slam.

"Mademoiselle—fare—well!"

"Drive on!" said Lady Mary.

M. Beaucaire followed the carriage with his eyes. As the noise of the wheels and the hoof-beats of the accompanying cavalcade grew fainter in the distance, the handkerchief he had held against his side dropped into the white dust, a heavy red splotch.

"Only—roses," he gasped, and fell back in the arms of his servants.

EAU NASH stood at the door of the rooms, smiling blandly upon a dainty throng in the pink of its finery and gay furbelows. The great exquisite bent his body constantly in a series of consummately adjusted bows: before a great dowager, seeming to sweep the floor in august deference; somewhat stately to the young bucks; greeting the wits with gracious

87

friendliness and a twinkle of raillery;
inclining with fatherly gallantry before the beauties; the degree of his
inclination measured the altitude of
the recipient as accurately as a nicely
calculated sand-glass measures the
hours.

The King of Bath was happy, for
wit, beauty, fashion—to speak more
concretely: nobles, belles, gamesters,
beaux, statesmen, and poets—made
fairyland (or opera bouffe, at least)
in his dominions; play ran higher
and higher, and Mr. Nash's coffers
filled up with gold. To crown his
pleasure, a prince of the French
blood, the young Comte de Beaujolais, just arrived from Paris, had
reached Bath at noon in state, ac-
companied by the Marquis de Mire-

poix, the ambassador of Louis XV. The Beau dearly prized the society of the lofty, and the present visit was an honor to Bath: hence to the Master of Ceremonies. What was better, there would be some profitable hours with the cards and dice. So it was that Mr. Nash smiled never more benignly than on that bright evening. The rooms rang with the silvery voices of women and delightful laughter, while the fiddles went merrily, their melodies chiming sweetly with the joyance of his mood.

The skill and brazen effrontery of the ambassador's scoundrelly servant in passing himself off for a man of condition formed the point of departure for every conversation. It was discovered that there were but three persons present who had not suspected him from the first; and, by a singular paradox, the most astute of all proved to be old Mr. Bicksit, the traveler, once a visitor at Chateau-rien; for he, according to report, had by a coup of diplomacy entrapped the impostor into an admission that there was no such place. However, like poor Captain Badger, the worthy old man had held his peace out of regard for the Duke of Winterset. This nobleman, heretofore secretly dis-liked, suspected of irregular devices at play, and never admired, had won admiration and popularity by his re-morse for the mistake, and by the modesty of his attitude in endeavor-ing to atone for it, without presum-ing upon the privilege of his rank to

laugh at the indignation of society;
an action the more praiseworthy
because his exposure of the impostor
entailed the disclosure of his own
culpability in having stood the villain's sponsor. To-night, the happy
gentleman, with Lady Mary Carlisle
upon his arm, went grandly about
the rooms, sowing and reaping a
harvest of smiles. 'Twas said work
would be begun at once to rebuild
the Duke's country seat, while several ruined Jews might be paid out
of prison. People gazing on the
beauty and the stately but modest
hero by her side, said they would
make a noble pair. She had long
been distinguished by his attentions,
and he had come brilliantly out of
the episode of the Frenchman, who

had been his only real rival. Wherever they went, there arose a buzz of pleasing gossip and adulation.

Mr. Nash, seeing them near him, came forward with greetings. A word on the side passed between the nobleman and the exquisite.

"I had news of the rascal tonight," whispered Nash. "He lay at a farm till yesterday, when he disappeared; his ruffians, too."

"You have arranged?" asked the Duke.

"Fourteen bailiffs are watching without. He could not come within gunshot. If they clap eyes on him, they will hustle him to jail, and his cutthroats shall not avail him a hair's weight. The impertinent swore he'd be here by nine, did he?"

"He said so; and 'tis a rash dog, sir."

"It is just nine now."

"Send out to see if they have taken him."

"Gladly." The Beau beckoned an attendant, and whispered in his ear.

Many of the crowd had edged up to the two gentlemen with apparent carelessness, to overhear their conversation. Those who did overhear repeated it in covert asides, and this circulating undertone, confirming a vague rumor that Beaucaire would attempt the entrance that night, lent a pleasurable color of excitement to the evening. The French prince, the ambassador, and their suites were announced. Polite as the assembly was, it was also curious, and there occurred a mannerly rush to see the newcomers. Lady Mary, already pale, grew whiter as the throng closed round her; she looked up pathetically at the Duke, who lost no time in extricating her from the pressure.

"Wait here," he said; "I will fetch you a glass of negus," and disappeared. He had not thought to bring a chair, and she, looking about with an increasing faintness and finding none, saw that she was standing by the door of a small side-room. The crowd swerved back for the passage of the legate of France, and pressed upon her. She opened the door, and went in.

The room was empty save for two

gentlemen, who were quietly playing cards at a table. They looked up as she entered. They were M. Beaucaire and Mr. Molyneux.

She uttered a quick cry and leaned against the wall, her hand to her breast. Beaucaire, though white and weak, had brought her a chair before Molyneux could stir.

"Mademoiselle——"

"Do not touch me!" she said, with such frozen abhorrence in her voice that he stopped short. "Mr. Molyneux, you seek strange company!"

"Madam," replied Molyneux, bowing deeply, as much to Beaucaire as to herself, "I am honored by the presence of both of you."

"Oh, are you mad!" she exclaimed, contemptuously.

"This gentleman has exalted me with his confidence, madam," he replied.

"Will you add your ruin to the scandal of this fellow's presence here? How he obtained entrance——"

"Pardon, mademoiselle," interrupted Beaucaire. "Did I not say I should come? M. Molyneux was so obliging as to answer for me to the fourteen frien's of M. de Winterset and *Meestaire* Nash."

"Do you not know," she turned vehemently upon Molyneux, "that he will be removed the moment I leave this room? Do you wish to be dragged out with him? For your sake, sir, because I have always thought you a man of heart, I give you a chance to save yourself from

disgrace—and—your companion from
jail. Let him slip out by some retired way, and you may give me
your arm and we will enter the next
room as if nothing had happened.
Come, sir——"

"Mademoiselle——"

"Mr. Molyneux, I desire to hear
nothing from your companion. Had
I not seen you at cards with him I
should have supposed him in attendance as your lackey. Do you desire
to take advantage of my offer, sir?"

"Mademoiselle, I could not tell
you, on that night——"

"You may inform your high-born
friend, Mr. Molyneux, that I heard
everything he had to say; that my
pride once had the pleasure of listening to his high-born confession!"

"Ah, it is gentle to taunt one with his birth, mademoiselle? Ah, no! There is a man in my country who say strange things of that—that a man is not his father, but *himself*."

"You may inform your friend, Mr. Molyneux, that he had a chance to defend himself against accusation; that he said all——"

"That I did say all I could have strength to say. Mademoiselle, you did not see—as it was right—that I had been stung by a big wasp. It was nothing, a scratch; but, mademoiselle, the sky went round and the moon dance' on the earth. I could not wish that big wasp to see he had stung me; so I mus' only say what I can have strength for, and stan' straight till he is gone. Beside',

there are other rizzons. Ah, you
mus' belief! My Molyneux I sen'
for, and tell him all, because he show
courtesy to the yo'ng Frenchman,
and I can trus' him. I trus' you,
mademoiselle—long ago—and would
have tol' you ev'rything, excep' jus'
because—well, for the romance, the
fon! You belief? It is so clearly
so; you do belief, mademoiselle?"

She did not even look at him. M.
Beaucaire lifted his hand appealingly
toward her. "Can there be no faith
in—in—" he said timidly, and
paused. She was silent, a statue, my
Lady Disdain.

"If you had not belief' me to be
an impostor; if I had never said I
was Chateaurien; if I had been jus'
that Monsieur Beaucaire of the story

99

they tol' you, but never with the *heart* of a lackey, an hones' man, a *man*, the man you knew, *himself*, could you—would you—" He was trying to speak firmly; yet, as he gazed upon her splendid beauty, he choked slightly, and fumbled in the lace at his throat with unsteady fingers.—"Would you—have let me ride by your side in the autumn moonlight?" Her glance passed by him as it might have passed by a footman or a piece of furniture. He was dressed magnificently, a multitude of orders glittering on his breast. Her eye took no knowledge of him.

"Mademoiselle—I have the honor to ask you: if you had known this Beaucaire was hones', though of peasant birth, would you——"

Involuntarily, controlled as her icy presence was, she shuddered. There was a moment of silence.

"Mr. Molyneux," said Lady Mary, "in spite of your discourtesy in allowing a servant to address me, I offer you a last chance to leave this room undisgraced. Will you give me your arm?"

"Pardon me, madam," said Mr. Molyneux.

Beaucaire dropped into a chair with his head bent low and his arm outstretched on the table; his eyes filled slowly in spite of himself, and two tears rolled down the young man's cheeks.

"An' live men are jus'—*names!*" said M. Beaucaire.

Chapter
Six

IN the outer room, Winterset, unable to find Lady Mary, and supposing her to have joined Lady Rellerton, disposed of his negus, then approached the two visitors to pay his respects to the young prince, whom he discovered to be a stripling of seventeen, arrogant-looking, but pretty as a girl. Standing beside the Marquis de Mirepoix—a man of quiet bearing—he was surrounded by a group of the great, among whom Mr. Nash naturally counted himself. The Beau was felicitating himself that the foreigners had not arrived a week earlier, in which case he and Bath would have been detected in a piece of gross ignorance concerning the French nobility—making much of de Mirepoix's ex-barber.

"'Tis a lucky thing that fellow was got out of the way," he ejaculated, under cover.

"Thank me for it," rejoined Winterset.

An attendant begged Mr. Nash's notice. The head bailiff sent word that Beaucaire had long since entered the building by a side door. It was supposed Mr. Nash had known of it,

and the Frenchman was not arrested,
as Mr. Molyneux was in his company, and said he would be answerable
for him.   Consternation was so plain
on the Beau's trained face that the
Duke leaned toward him anxiously.

"The villain's in, and Molyneux
hath gone mad!"

Mr. Bantison, who had been
fiercely elbowing his way toward
them, joined heads with them. "You
may well say he is in," he exclaimed,
"and if you want to know where,
why, in yonder card-room. I saw
him through the half-open door."

"What's to be done?" asked the
Beau.

"Send the bailiffs——"

"Fie, fie!   A file of bailiffs? The
scandal!"

"Then listen to me," said the Duke. "I'll select half-a-dozen gentlemen, explain the matter, and we'll put him in the center of us and take him out to the bailiffs. 'Twill appear nothing. Do you remain here and keep the attention of Beaujolais and de Mirepoix. Come, Bantison, fetch Townbrake and Harry Rakell yonder; I'll bring the others."

Three minutes later, his Grace of Winterset flung wide the card-room door, and, after his friends had entered, closed it.

"Ah!" remarked M. Beaucaire quietly. "Six more large men."

The Duke, seeing Lady Mary, started; but the angry signs of her interview had not left her face, and reassured him. He offered his hand to conduct her to the door. "May I have the honor?"

"If this is to be known, 'twill be better if I leave after; I should be observed if I went now."

"As you will, madam," he answered, not displeased. "And now, you impudent villain," he began, turning to M. Beaucaire, but to fall back astounded. "'Od's blood, the dog hath murdered and robbed some royal prince!" He forgot Lady Mary's presence in his excitement. "Lay hands on him!" he shouted. "Tear those orders from him!"

Molyneux threw himself between. "One word!" he cried. "One word before you offer an outrage you will repent all your lives!"

"Or let M. de Winterset come alone," laughed M. Beaucaire.

"Do you expect me to fight a cut-throat barber, and with bare hands?"

"I think one does not expec' monsieur to fight anybody. Would *I* fight you, you think? That was why I had my servants, that evening we play. I would gladly fight almos' any one in the worl'; but I did not wish to soil my hand with a——"

"Stuff his lying mouth with his orders!" shouted the Duke.

But Molyneux still held the gentlemen back. "One moment," he cried.

"M. de Winterset," said Beaucaire, "of what are you afraid? You calculate well. Beaucaire might have been belief'—an impostor that you yourself expose'? Never! But I was not goin' reveal that secret. You have not absolve me of my promise."

"Tell what you like," answered the Duke. "Tell all the wild lies you have time for. You have five minutes to make up your mind to go quietly."

"Now you absolve me, then? Ha, ha! Oh, yes! Mademoiselle," he bowed to Lady Mary, "I have the honor to reques' you leave the room. You shall miss no details if these frien's of yours kill me, on the honor of a French gentleman."

"A French what?" laughed Bantison.

"Do you dare keep up the pretense?" cried Lord Townbrake. "Know, you villain barber, that your master, the Marquis de Mirepoix, is in the next room."

Molyneux heaved a great sigh of relief. " Shall I—" He turned to M. Beaucaire.

The young man laughed, and said: " Tell him come here at once."

"Impudent to the last!" cried Bantison, as Molyneux hurried from the room.

"Now you goin' to see M. Beaucaire's master," said Beaucaire to Lady Mary. "'Tis true what I say, the other night. I cross from France in his suite; my passport say as his barber. Then to pass the *ennui* of exile, I come to Bath and play for what one will. It kill the time. But when the people hear I have been a servant they come only secretly; and there is

one of them—he has absolve' me of
a promise not to speak—of him I
learn something he cannot wish to be
tol'.   I make some trouble to learn
this thing.   Why I should do this?
Well—that is my own rizzon.   So I
make this man help me in a masque,
the unmasking it was, for, as there is
no one to know me, I throw off my
black wig and become myself—and
so I am 'Chateaurien,' Castle Nowhere. Then this man I use', this
Winterset, he——"

"I have great need to deny these
accusations?" said the Duke.

"Nay," said Lady Mary wearily.

"Shall I tell you why I mus' be
'Victor' and 'Beaucaire' and 'Chateaurien,' and not myself?"

"To escape from the bailiffs for

debts for razors and soap," gibed Lord Townbrake.

"No, monsieur. In France I have got a cousin who is a man with a very bad temper at some time', and he will never enjoy his relatives to do what he does not wish——"

He was interrupted by a loud commotion from without. The door was flung open, and the young Count of Beaujolais bounded in and threw his arms about the neck of M. Beaucaire.

"Philippe!" he cried. "My brother, I have come to take you back with me."

M. de Mirepoix followed him, bowing as a courtier, in deference; but M. Beaucaire took both his hands heartily. Molyneux came after, with Mr. Nash, and closed the door.

"My warmest felicitations," said the Marquis. "There is no longer need for your incognito."

"Thou best of masters!" said Beaucaire, touching him fondly on the shoulder. "I know. Your courier came safely. And so I am forgiven! But I forget." He turned to the lady. She had begun to tremble exceedingly. "Faires' of all the English fair," he said, as the gentlemen bowed low to her deep courtesy, "I beg the honor to presen' to Lady Mary Carlisle, M. le Comte de Beaujolais. M. de Mirepoix has already the honor. Lady Mary has been very kind to me, my frien's; you mus' help me make my acknowledgment. Mademoiselle and gentlemen, will you give

me that favor to detain you one
instan'?"

"Henri," he turned to the young
Beaujolais, "I wish you had shared
my masque—I have been so gay!"
The surface of his tone was merry,
but there was an undercurrent, weary-
sad, to speak of what was the mood,
not the manner. He made the effect
of addressing every one present, but
he looked steadily at Lady Mary.
Her eyes were fixed upon him,
with a silent and frightened fas-
cination, and she trembled more and
more. "I am a great actor, Henri.
These gentlemen are yet scarce con-
vince' I am not a lackey! And I mus'
tell you that I was jus' now to be expelled for having been a barber!"

"Oh, no!" the ambassador cried

out. "He would not be content with me; he would wander over a strange country."

"Ha, ha, my Mirepoix! And what is better, one evening I am oblige' to fight some frien's of M. de Winterset there, and some ladies and cavaliers look on, and they still think me a servant. Oh, I am a great actor! 'Tis true there is not a peasant in France who would not have then known one 'born'; but they are wonderful, this English people, holding by an idea once it is in their heads—a mos' worthy quality. But my good Molyneux here, he had speak to me with courtesy, jus' because I am a man an' jus' because he is al—ways kind. (I have learn' that his great-grandfather was a Frenchman.) So I sen' to him and tell him ev'rything, and he gain admittance for me here to-night to await my frien's.

" I was speaking to messieurs about my cousin, who will meddle in the affair' of his relative'. Well, that gentleman, he make a marriage for me with a good and accomplish' lady, very noble and very beautiful— and amiable." (The young count at his elbow started slightly at this, but immediately appeared to wrap himself in a mantle of solemn thought.) " Unfortunately, when my cousin arrange' so, I was a dolt, a little blockhead; I swear to marry for myself and when I please, or never if I like. That lady is all things charming and gentle, and, in truth, she is—very much attach' to me—why should I

not say it? I am so proud of it.
She is very faithful and forgiving and
sweet; she would be the same, I
think, if I—were even—a lackey.
But I? I was a dolt, a little unsen-
sible brute; I did not value such
thing' then; I was too yo'ng, las'
June. So I say to my cousin, 'No,
I make my own choosing!' 'Little
fool,' he answer, 'she is the one for
you. Am I not wiser than you?'
And he was very angry, and, as he
has influence in France, word come'
that he will get me put in Vincennes,
so I mus' run away quick till his
anger is gone. My good frien' Mirepoix is jus' leaving for London; he
take' many risk' for my sake; his
hairdresser die before he start', so I
travel as that poor barber. But my

cousin is a man to be afraid of when he is angry, even in England, and I mus' not get my Mirepoix in trouble. I mus' not be discover' till my cousin is ready to laugh about it all and make it a joke. And there may be spies; so I change my name again, and come to Bath to amuse my retreat with a little gaming—I am al—ways fond of that. But three day' ago M. le Marquis send me a courier to say that my brother, who know where I had run away, is come from France to say that my cousin is appease'; he need me for his little theatre, the play cannot go on. I do not need to espouse mademoiselle. All shall be forgiven if I return, and my brother and M. de Mirepoix will meet me in Bath to felicitate.

"There is one more thing to say, that is all. I have said I learn' a secret, and use it to make a man introduce me if I will not tell. He has absolve' me of that promise. My fren's, I had not the wish to ruin that man. I was not receive'; *Meestaire* Nash had reboff me; I had no other way excep' to use this fellow. So I say, 'Take me to Lady Malbourne's ball as "Chateaurien."' I throw off my wig, and shave, and behol', I am M. le Duc de Castle Nowhere. Ha, ha! You see?"

The young man's manner suddenly changed. He became haughty, menacing. He stretched out his arm, and pointed at Winterset. "Now I am no 'Beaucaire,' messieurs. I am a French gentleman. The man who introduce' me at the price of his honor, and then betray' me to redeem it, is that coward, that card-cheat there!''

Winterset made a horrible effort to laugh. The gentlemen who surrounded him fell away as from pestilence. "A French gentleman!" he sneered savagely, and yet fearfully. "I don't know who you are. Hide behind as many toys and ribbons as you like; I'll know the name of the man who dares bring such a charge!"

"Sir!" cried de Mirepoix sharply, advancing a step towards him; but he checked himself at once. He made a low bow of state, first to the young Frenchman, then to Lady Mary and the company. "Permit me, Lady Mary and gentlemen," he said, "to assume the honor of presenting you to His Highness, Prince Louis-Philippe de Valois, Duke of Orleans, Duke of Chartres, Duke of Nemours, Duke of Montpensier, First Prince of the Blood Royal, First Peer of France, Lieutenant-General of French Infantry, Governor of Dauphiné, Knight of the Golden Fleece, Grand Master of the Order of Notre Dame, of Mount Carmel, and of St. Lazarus in Jerusalem; and cousin to His most Christian Majesty, Louis the Fifteenth, King of France."

"Those are a few of my brother's names," whispered Henri of Beaujolais to Molyneux. "Old Mirepoix has the long breath, but it take' a strong man two day' to say all of them. I can suppose this Winterset know' now who bring the charge!"

"Castle Nowhere!" gasped Beau Nash, falling back upon the burly prop of Mr. Bantison's shoulder.

"The Duke of Orleans will receive a message from me within the hour!" said Winterset, as he made his way to the door. His face was black with rage and shame.

"I tol' you that I would not soil my hand with you," answered the young man. "If you send a message no gentleman will bring it. Whoever shall bear it will receive a little beating from François."

He stepped to Lady Mary's side. Her head was bent low, her face averted. She seemed to breathe with difficulty, and leaned heavily upon a chair. "Monseigneur," she faltered in a half whisper, "can you—forgive me? It is a bitter—mistake—I have made. Forgive."

"Forgive?" he answered, and his voice was as broken as hers; but he went on, more firmly: "It is—nothing—less than nothing. There is—only jus' one—in the—whole worl' who would not have treat' me the way that you treat' me. It is to her that I am goin' to make reparation. You know something, Henri? I am not goin' back only because the king forgive' me. I am goin' to *please* him; I am goin' to espouse mademoiselle, our cousin. My frien's, I ask your felicitations."

"And the king does not compel him!" exclaimed young Henri.

"Henri, you want to fight me?" cried his brother sharply. "Don' you think the King of France is a wiser man than me?"

He offered his hand to Lady Mary.

"Mademoiselle is fatigue'. Will she honor me?"

He walked with her to the door, her hand fluttering faintly in his. From somewhere about the garments of one of them a little cloud of faded rose-leaves fell, and lay strewn on the floor behind them. He opened the door, and the lights shone on a multitude of eager faces turned toward it. There was a great hum of voices, and, over all, the fiddles wove a wandering air, a sweet French song of the *voyageur*.

He bowed very low, as, with fixed

and glistening eyes, Lady Mary Carlisle, the Beauty of Bath, passed slowly by him and went out of the room.

THE END

DATE DUE

Baking
Is
Fun
Volume 10

Recipes No. 751-825

*I*ntroduction

Dear Reader:

Thank you for purchasing the 10th Volume in our series, "Baking is Fun".

This volume offers you a collection of treasured family favourites from the private recipe collections of our Austrian neighbours.

Our collection treats you to a fine selection of tortes, cakes, cookies, breads, pastries and desserts. Accompanying every recipe is a full colour photograph inviting and enticing you. We are certain you will enjoy the variety of recipes this book has to offer.

From our kitchen to yours, we wish you joyful baking and Guten Appetit!

Additional copies of this book may be obtained by writing to:

oetker Recipe Service
2229 Drew Road
Mississauga, Ontario
L5S 1E5

Contents

Specialty Tortes

Biedermeier House Torte

Biedermeier Haustorte

Recipe No. 751

Batter:

5	egg yolks	5
250 g	sugar	1¼ cups
1 pkg	**oetker** vanilla sugar (9 g)	1 pkg
30 mL	water	2 tbsp
250 g	all-purpose flour	1¼ cups
1 pkg	**oetker** baking powder (14 g)	1 pkg
5	egg whites	5
1 pkg	**oetker** vanilla pudding (43 g)	1 pkg
125 mL	whipping cream	½ cup
15 mL	rum	1 tbsp

Filling:

250 g	butter	1¼ cups
250 g	icing sugar, sifted	2¼ cups
1 pkg	**oetker** vanilla sugar (9 g)	1 pkg
½ btl	**oetker** rum flavouring concentrate (1 mL)	½ btl
100 g	semi-sweet chocolate, softened	4 squares

Brushing:

125 mL	apricot jam	½ cup

Decoration:

some	chocolate sprinkles	some

Dusting:

some	icing sugar, sifted	some

Batter:

PREHEAT oven to 180°C (350°F). Grease one 20 cm (8") and one 13 cm (5") springform pan.

IN a mixing bowl, combine egg yolks, sugar, vanilla sugar and water. Beat until fluffy.

SIFT flour and baking powder over the egg yolk mixture. Fold in gently but thoroughly.

BEAT egg whites to stiff peaks. (Peaks should be so stiff that when a knife is inserted, the cut remains visible.)

FOLD beaten egg whites, vanilla pudding powder, whipping cream and rum into the egg yolk mixture, gently but thoroughly.

TURN three-quarters of the mixture into the larger prepared pan. Smooth surface with a knife.

TURN remaining mixture into the smaller prepared pan. Smooth surface with a knife.

BAKE for 30-40 minutes.

LET tortes cool completely in their pans.

LOOSEN edges of tortes with a knife.

CAREFULLY remove from pans.

Filling:

IN a mixing bowl, beat butter until fluffy.

ADD icing sugar, vanilla sugar, flavouring concentrate, and chocolate. Fold in gently but thoroughly.

SLICE each torte once to make two layers.

SPREAD three-quarters of the filling evenly over bottom layers. Assemble tortes.

SPREAD jam evenly over surface of tortes.

SPREAD remaining filling on sides of both tortes.

DECORATE sides with chocolate sprinkles.

PLACE the smaller torte in the centre of the large torte.

DUST surface of smaller torte with icing sugar.

8

Grandmother's Specialty Torte

Großmutters Spezialtorte

Recipe No. 752

Ingredients:

125 mL	water	½ cup	
150 g	icing sugar, sifted	1⅓ cups	
150 g	hazelnuts, ground	1½ cups	
170 g	semi-sweet chocolate, chopped	6 squares	
6	egg yolks	6	
30 mL	bread crumbs	2 tbsp	
6	egg whites	6	

Filling:

250 mL	whipping cream	1 cup	
1 pkg	**oetker** vanilla sugar (9 g)	1 pkg	
250 g	milk chocolate	9 squares	

Brushing:

150 mL	apricot jam	⅔ cup	

Glaze:

1 pkg	**oetker** Chocofix (100 g)	1 pkg	

PREHEAT oven to 180°C (350°F). Grease and flour a 25 cm (10") springform pan.
IN a saucepan, bring water to a boil.
ADD icing sugar, hazelnuts and chocolate.
STIR until chocolate has melted.
REMOVE from heat. Cool completely.

ADD egg yolks and bread crumbs. Stir well.
BEAT egg whites to stiff peaks. (Peaks should be so stiff that when a knife is inserted, the cut remains visible.)
FOLD beaten egg whites into the egg yolk mixture, gently but thoroughly.

TURN mixture into prepared pan.
SMOOTH surface with a knife.
BAKE for 60-65 minutes. Let cool.

LOOSEN edges of torte with a knife. Carefully remove pan ring.

Filling:

IN a saucepan, combine whipping cream, vanilla sugar and chocolate.
BRING mixture to a boil, stirring constantly.
REMOVE from heat. Let cool.
WHEN whipped cream mixture has cooled completely, beat until fluffy.

SLICE torte once to make two layers.
SPREAD filling on bottom layer. Top with second layer.
SPREAD jam over top and sides of torte.

Glaze:

PREPARE Chocofix according to package directions.
GLAZE torte.

Toscana Torte

Toskanatorte

Recipe No. 753

Batter:

2	eggs	2
120 g	sugar	⅔ cup
1 pkg	**oetker** vanilla sugar (9 g)	1 pkg
pinch	salt	pinch
110 g	butter, melted	½ cup
140 g	all-purpose flour	1¼ cups
5 mL	**oetker** baking powder	1 tsp

Topping:

60 g	butter	¼ cup
80 g	sugar	⅓ cup
45 mL	whipping cream	3 tbsp
15 mL	all-purpose flour, sifted	1 tbsp
200 g	almonds, sliced	2 cups

Batter:

PREHEAT oven to 200°C (400°F). Grease a 25 cm (10") springform pan. Sprinkle with bread crumbs.

IN a mixing bowl, combine eggs, sugar, vanilla sugar and salt.

BEAT until fluffy.

STIR in butter.

SIFT flour and baking powder over the egg mixture. Fold in gently but thoroughly.

TURN batter into prepared pan.

SMOOTH surface with a knife.

BAKE for 20 minutes.

Topping:

IN a saucepan, combine butter, sugar and whipping cream. Bring to a boil, stirring constantly.

REMOVE from heat.

FOLD in flour and almonds. Let cool.

SPREAD mixture evenly over hot torte.

RETURN to oven.

BAKE for another 20 minutes. Let cool.

LOOSEN edges of torte with a knife. Carefully remove pan ring.

"Sunshine" Torte

Haustorte "Sonnhalber"

Recipe No. 754

Batter:

5	eggs	5
110 g	sugar	½ cup
1 pkg	**oetker** vanilla sugar (9 g)	1 pkg
120 g	almonds, ground	1½ cups
45 mL	bread crumbs	3 tbsp
15 mL	cocoa, sifted	1 tbsp
50 g	all-purpose flour	⅓ cup
5 mL	**oetker** baking powder	1 tsp

Filling:

250 mL	whipping cream	1 cup
1 pkg	**oetker** Whip it (10 g)	1 pkg
1 pkg	**oetker** vanilla sugar (9 g)	1 pkg
125 mL	cranberry jam	½ cup

Brushing:

80 mL	apricot jam, heated	⅓ cup

Glaze and Decoration:

100 g	icing sugar, sifted	1 cup
5 mL	instant coffee	1 tsp
30 mL	rum	2 tbsp
16	mocha beans	16

Batter:
PREHEAT oven to 160°C (325°F). Grease a 25 cm (10") springform pan.
IN a mixing bowl, beat eggs, sugar and vanilla sugar until fluffy.
STIR in almonds, bread crumbs and cocoa.
SIFT flour and baking powder over the egg mixture. Fold in gently but thoroughly.

TURN mixture into prepared pan.
SMOOTH surface with a knife.
BAKE for 35-40 minutes. Let cool.

LOOSEN edges of torte with a knife. Carefully remove pan ring.

Filling:
IN a mixing bowl, beat whipping cream, Whip it and vanilla sugar to stiff peaks.

SLICE torte once to make two layers.
SPREAD one-half of the whipped cream evenly over the bottom layer. Reserve remaining whipped cream.
SPREAD cranberry jam evenly over the whipped cream. Top with second layer. Lightly press down on top layer.
BRUSH apricot jam over top of the torte.

Glaze and Decoration:
COMBINE icing sugar, instant coffee and rum. Mix well.
GLAZE torte.
BEFORE the glaze has set completely, decorate with reserved whipped cream and mocha beans.

14

Apple-Nut Torte

Apfel-Nußtorte

Recipe No. 755

Batter:

180 g	butter, softened	¾ cup	
250 g	sugar	1¼ cups	
1 pkg	**oetker** vanilla sugar (9 g)	1 pkg	
pinch	salt	pinch	
5 mL	cinnamon	1 tsp	
3	eggs	3	
300 g	all-purpose flour	2 cups	
10 mL	**oetker** baking powder	2 tsp	
100 g	walnuts, coarsely chopped	1 cup	
500 mL	apples, peeled, cored and grated	2 cups	

Brushing:

125 mL	apple jam	½ cup	

Glaze:

100 g	icing sugar, sifted	¾ cup	
45 mL	rum	3 tbsp	

Batter:

PREHEAT oven to 180°C (350°F). Grease a 25 cm (10") springform pan. Sprinkle with bread crumbs.

IN a mixing bowl, beat butter until fluffy.

GRADUALLY beat in sugar, vanilla sugar, salt, cinnamon and eggs.

SIFT flour and baking powder over the butter mixture. Add nuts. Fold in gently but thoroughly.

ADD grated apples to butter mixture. Mix well.

TURN batter into prepared pan.

SMOOTH surface with a knife.

BAKE for 60-65 minutes.

LOOSEN the edges of the warm torte with a knife. Carefully remove pan ring.

HEAT the jam slightly.

SPREAD jam over sides and top of torte.

COOL completely.

Glaze:

IN a mixing bowl, combine icing sugar and rum.

STIR until smooth.

DECORATE sides and top of torte with glaze.

Egg Liqueur Torte

Eierlikörtorte

Recipe No. 756

Batter:

5	egg yolks	5
125 mL	vegetable oil	½ cup
125 mL	lukewarm water	½ cup
150 g	icing sugar, sifted	1⅓ cups
150 g	almonds, ground	1½ cups
5	egg whites	5
140 g	all-purpose flour	1¼ cups
1 pkg	**oetker** baking powder (14 g)	1 pkg

Filling:

125 mL	red currant jam	½ cup

Decoration:

250 mL	whipping cream	1 cup
1 pkg	**oetker** Whip it (10 g)	1 pkg
1 pkg	**oetker** vanilla sugar (9 g)	1 pkg
50 mL	egg liqueur	¼ cup

Batter:

PREHEAT oven to 180°C (350°F). Grease and flour a 25 cm (10") springform pan.

IN a mixing bowl, combine egg yolks, vegetable oil, water, icing sugar and almonds. Beat until fluffy.

IN another bowl, beat egg whites to stiff peaks. (Peaks should be so stiff that when a knife is inserted, the cut remains visible.)

FOLD beaten egg whites into egg yolk mixture, gently but thoroughly.

SIFT flour and baking powder over the egg mixture. Mix well.

TURN batter into prepared pan.

SMOOTH surface with a knife.

BAKE for 45 minutes. Let cool.

LOOSEN edges of torte with a knife. Carefully remove pan ring.

SLICE the torte once to make two layers.

SPREAD jam evenly over bottom layer. Top with second layer.

IN a mixing bowl, beat whipping cream, Whip it and vanilla sugar to stiff peaks.

SPREAD two-thirds of the whipped cream over the sides and top of the torte.

PLACE remaining whipped cream in a pastry bag fitted with a round tube.

PIPE a border around the top edge of the torte.

POUR egg liqueur over the surface of the torte.

Strawberry Rice Torte

Erdbeer-Reis-Torte

Recipe No. 757

Batter:

5	egg yolks	5
125 g	sugar	⅔ cup
1 pkg	**oetker** vanilla sugar (9 g)	1 pkg
½ btl	**oetker** lemon flavouring concentrate (1 mL)	½ btl
pinch	salt	pinch
5	egg whites	5
65 g	all-purpose flour	½ cup
65 g	**oetker** Gustin corn starch	½ cup
60 mL	butter, melted	¼ cup

Filling:

500 mL	milk	2 cups
1 pkg	**oetker** vanilla sugar (9 g)	1 pkg
pinch	salt	pinch
80 g	rice, long grain	⅓ cup
1 pkg	gelatin (dissolved in 45 mL/ 3 tbsp boiling water)	1 pkg
250 mL	whipping cream	1 cup
50 g	sugar	¼ cup
500 g	fresh strawberries, chopped	4 cups
15 mL	Cointreau	1 tbsp

Topping and Decoration:

1 kg	strawberries	8 cups
1 pkg	**oetker** vanilla sugar (9 g)	1 pkg
50 g	pistachio nuts, chopped	⅓ cup

Batter:

PREHEAT oven to 180°C (350°F). Grease a 25 cm (10") springform pan.

IN a double boiler, beat egg yolks, sugar, vanilla sugar, lemon flavouring concentrate and salt until fluffy. Let cool.

IN a mixing bowl, beat egg whites to stiff peaks. (Peaks should be so stiff that when a knife is inserted, the cut remains visible.)

FOLD beaten egg whites into egg yolk mixture, gently but thoroughly.

SIFT flour and corn starch over the egg mixture.

ADD butter. Fold in gently but thoroughly.

TURN batter into prepared pan.
SMOOTH surface with a knife.
BAKE for 25-30 minutes.
LET cool.

Filling:

IN a saucepan, bring milk, vanilla sugar and salt to a boil.

STIR in rice. Reduce heat and simmer, covered, for 45 minutes.

STIR gelatin into rice mixture. Mix well.
COOL completely.

IN a mixing bowl, beat whipping cream and sugar to stiff peaks.

FOLD whipped cream, strawberries and Cointreau into rice mixture.

USING a knife, loosen edges of torte from pan.

CAREFULLY remove pan ring.
SLICE torte once to make two layers.
REMOVE top layer. Reposition pan ring.
SPREAD filling evenly over bottom cake layer.
TOP with second layer.
CHILL for one hour.

Topping and Decoration:

PURÉE 500 mL (2 cups) of the strawberries with vanilla sugar. Spread on top of torte.
DECORATE with remaining strawberries.
SPRINKLE with pistachio nuts.

19

Swedish Torte

Schwedentorte

Recipe No. 758

Ingredients:

5	egg whites	5
200 g	sugar	1 cup
1 pkg	**oetker** vanilla sugar (9 g)	1 pkg
150 g	almonds, ground	1¼ cups

Spreading and Sprinkling:

750 mL	whipping cream	3 cups
120 g	bitter chocolate, shaved	4 squares

Decoration:

50 g	semi-sweet chocolate	2 squares

PREHEAT oven to 140°C (275°F).
IN a mixing bowl, beat egg whites, sugar and vanilla sugar to stiff peaks.
FOLD in almonds, gently but thoroughly.

DRAW circles, 25 cm (10") in diameter, on four pieces of parchment paper.
SPREAD egg white mixture ½ cm (³⁄₁₆") thick within the four circles.
PLACE each piece of paper on a baking sheet.
BAKE individually for 20-25 minutes.

AFTER baking, remove paper from layers immediately. Cool completely.
REPEAT process for remaining layers.

Spreading and Sprinkling:
BEAT whipping cream to stiff peaks.
REFRIGERATE one-quarter of the whipped cream.
SPREAD three of the layers evenly with whipped cream.
SPRINKLE each layer with chocolate.
ASSEMBLE torte.
TOP with remaining layer.
SPREAD refrigerated whipped cream evenly over sides and top of torte.
CHILL overnight.

Decoration:
IN a double boiler, heat chocolate until it reaches a temperature of 32°C (90°F).
POUR chocolate onto a marble or glass surface.
SPREAD evenly over surface.
ALLOW chocolate to set (not harden!). Using a scraper, push chocolate forward creating curls.
PLACE chocolate curls in a star pattern on top of the torte.

Suggestion: Serve frozen.

21

*R*ed Wine Torte

Rotweintorte

Recipe No. 759

Batter:

220	g	butter	1 cup
250	g	icing sugar, sifted	2¼ cups
1	pkg	**oetker** vanilla sugar (9 g)	1 pkg
4		egg yolks	4
100	g	semi-sweet chocolate, shaved	4 squares
5	mL	cinnamon	1 tsp
15	mL	cocoa	1 tbsp
125	mL	red wine	½ cup
250	g	all-purpose flour	1¾ cups
½	pkg	**oetker** baking powder (7 g)	½ pkg
4		egg whites	4

Red Wine Glaze:

150	g	icing sugar, sifted	1⅓ cups
60-75	mL	red wine, heated	4-5 tbsp

Batter:
PREHEAT oven to 180°C (350°F). Grease and flour a 25 cm (10") springform pan.
IN a mixing bowl, beat butter until fluffy.
GRADUALLY beat in icing sugar, vanilla sugar and egg yolks.
STIR in chocolate, cinnamon, cocoa and red wine.
IN another bowl, sift together flour and baking powder. Stir into butter mixture.

BEAT egg whites to stiff peaks. (Peaks should be so stiff that when a knife is inserted, the cut remains visible.)
FOLD beaten egg whites into butter mixture, gently but thoroughly.

TURN batter into prepared pan.
BAKE for 65 minutes. Cool completely.

USING a knife, loosen edges of torte from pan. Carefully remove pan ring.

Glaze:
IN a mixing bowl, combine icing sugar and wine.
GLAZE torte

Zucchini Torte

Zucchinitorte

Recipe No. 760

Batter:

3	egg yolks	3
370 g	sugar	1¼ cups
600 mL	zucchini, grated	2½ cups
175 mL	vegetable oil	¾ cup
370 g	all-purpose flour, sifted	2¼ cups
2 mL	**oetker** baking powder	½ tsp
2 mL	baking soda	½ tsp
5 mL	cinnamon	1 tsp
150 g	walnuts or hazelnuts, ground	1½ cups
3	egg whites	3

Brushing:

125 mL	red currant jam	½ cup

Glaze:

1 pkg	**oetker** Chocofix (100 g)	1 pkg

Batter:

PREHEAT oven to 180°C (350°F). Grease and flour a 25 cm (10") springform pan.

IN a mixing bowl, beat egg yolks and sugar until fluffy.

STIR in zucchini and vegetable oil.

IN another bowl, mix together flour, baking powder, baking soda, cinnamon and nuts.

FOLD into egg mixture, gently but thoroughly.

BEAT egg whites to stiff peaks. (Peaks should be so stiff that when a knife is inserted, the cut remains visible.)

FOLD into flour-egg mixture.

TURN batter into prepared pan.

SMOOTH surface with a knife.

BAKE for 70-75 minutes. Let cool.

USING a knife, loosen edges of torte from pan. Carefully remove pan ring.

SPREAD jam evenly over top and sides of torte.

Glaze:

PREPARE Chocofix according to package directions. Glaze torte.

BEFORE the Chocofix sets, draw lines on the surface of the torte with a knife.

Poppy Seed Quark Torte

Mohn-Topfentorte

Recipe No. 761

Batter:

110 g	butter	½	cup
50 mL	icing sugar, sifted	¼	cup
1 pkg	**oetker** vanilla sugar (9 g)	1	pkg
5 mL	cinnamon	1	tsp
pinch	salt		pinch
4	egg yolks	4	
4	egg whites	4	
80 g	sugar	⅓	cup
150 g	poppy seeds, ground	1⅔	cups
70 g	hazelnuts, ground	¾	cup

Filling:

250 g	quark	1	cup
100 g	icing sugar, sifted	¾	cup
	juice of ½ lemon		
	grated peel of ½ lemon		
1 pkg	**oetker** vanilla sugar (9 g)	1	pkg
pinch	salt		pinch
500 mL	whipping cream	2	cups
1 pkg	gelatin (dissolved in 45 mL/3 tbsp boiling water)	1	pkg

Topping:

60 g	icing sugar, sifted	½	cup
625 mL	raspberries	2½	cups
½ pkg	gelatin (dissolved in 30 mL/2 tbsp boiling water)	½	pkg

Decoration:

16	raspberries	16	

Batter:
PREHEAT oven to 180°C (350°F). Grease a 25 cm (10") springform pan.
IN a mixing bowl, beat butter, icing sugar, vanilla sugar, cinnamon and salt until fluffy.
ADD egg yolks, one at a time, beating after each addition.
IN another bowl, beat egg whites and sugar to stiff peaks.
FOLD beaten egg whites into the butter mixture, gently but thoroughly.
MIX together poppy seeds and hazelnuts.
SPRINKLE over the butter mixture. Fold in gently but thoroughly.

TURN batter into prepared pan.
BAKE for 40 minutes.
COOL completely.

Filling:
IN a mixing bowl, beat quark, icing sugar, lemon juice and peel, vanilla sugar and salt.
IN another bowl, beat whipping cream to stiff peaks.
FOLD whipping cream and gelatin into the quark mixture, gently but thoroughly.

LOOSEN edges of torte from pan with a knife.
REMOVE pan ring. Clean and replace.
SPREAD quark mixture evenly over torte.
SMOOTH surface with a knife.
CHILL for 2-3 hours.

Topping:
SPRINKLE icing sugar over raspberries.
STRAIN raspberries into a saucepan. Heat slightly.
FOLD gelatin into raspberry mixture. Stir well.
SPREAD raspberry mixture evenly over quark mixture.
SMOOTH surface with a knife.
REFRIGERATE until set.
DECORATE with raspberries.
CAREFULLY remove pan ring.

Lemon Cloud Torte

Wolkentorte

Recipe No. 762

Batter:

110	g	butter	½	cup
125	g	sugar	⅔	cup
1	pkg	**oetker** vanilla sugar (9 g)	1	pkg
4		egg yolks	4	
150	g	all-purpose flour, sifted	1¼	cups
10	mL	**oetker** baking powder	2	tsp
60	mL	milk	¼	cup

Meringue:

4		egg whites	4	
200	g	icing sugar, sifted	1⅔	cups

Filling:

1		egg yolk	1	
110	g	sugar	½	cup
		juice of 2 lemons		
		grated peel of 1 lemon		
125	mL	water	½	cup
15	mL	**oetker** Gustin corn starch	1	tbsp
500	mL	whipping cream	2	cups

Batter:
PREHEAT oven to 180°C (350°F). Grease a 25 cm (10") springform pan.
IN a mixing bowl, beat butter until fluffy.
GRADUALLY beat in sugar, vanilla sugar and egg yolks.
IN another bowl, mix together flour and baking powder.
FOLD into butter mixture.
ADD milk. Mix well.
DIVIDE batter into two equal parts.
TURN one-half of the batter into prepared pan.
SMOOTH surface with a knife.

Meringue:
BEAT egg whites to soft peaks. Gradually beat in icing sugar until stiff peaks form. (Peaks should be so stiff that when a knife is inserted, the cut remains visible.)
DIVIDE beaten egg whites into two equal parts.
SPREAD one-half of the egg white mixture over the batter in the pan.
USING a knife, create a cloud-like pattern on the meringue.
BAKE on lower oven rack for 30 minutes. Let cool.

USING a knife, loosen edges of torte.
CAREFULLY remove pan ring.
REPEAT process for other half of batter.

Filling:
IN a saucepan, combine egg yolk, sugar, lemon juice, lemon peel, water and corn starch.
STIRRING constantly, bring mixture to a boil.
REMOVE from heat. Let cool.
BEAT whipping cream to stiff peaks.
FOLD into egg yolk mixture, gently but thoroughly.

TURN one torte layer, meringue side down, onto a serving plate.
SPREAD filling evenly over surface of torte.
TOP with second layer, meringue side up.

Russian Pluck Torte

Russische Zupftorte (Altes Zarenrezept)

Recipe No. 763

Dough:

300 g	all-purpose flour, sifted	2¼	cups
½ pkg	**oetker** baking powder (7 g)	½	pkg
200 g	icing sugar, sifted	1¼	cups
1	egg	1	
75 mL	cocoa	⅓	cup
220 g	butter, softened	1	cup

Filling:

220 g	butter	1	cup
200 g	sugar	1	cup
1 pkg	**oetker** vanilla sugar (9 g)	1	pkg
	grated peel of 1 lemon		
1 pkg	**oetker** vanilla pudding (43 g)	1	pkg
500 g	cream cheese, softened	2	cups
3	eggs	3	

Sprinkling:

some	icing sugar, sifted	some	

Dough:

PREHEAT oven to 180°C (350°F). Grease a 25 cm (10") springform pan.
SIFT flour and baking powder onto a working surface.
MAKE a well in the centre.
PUT icing sugar, egg and cocoa in the well.
CUT butter in small pieces over the ingredients in the well.
COVER with flour.
STARTING from the centre, work all ingredients into a smooth dough.
CHILL for 30 minutes.

Filling:

IN a mixing bowl, beat butter, sugar and vanilla sugar until fluffy. Gradually beat in lemon peel, pudding powder, cream cheese and eggs.

DIVIDE dough into two equal parts.
PRESS one-half of the dough in the bottom and up the sides of the pan.
POUR filling over dough. Smooth surface with a knife.
TEAR remaining half of dough into 1 cm (⅜") pieces. Flatten slightly.
COVER filling with pieces of dough.
BAKE for 60-70 minutes.
LET cool.

USING a knife, loosen edges of torte from pan. Carefully remove pan ring.
DUST surface of torte with icing sugar.

Waller Nut Torte

Wallersee-Torte

Recipe No. 764

Ingredients:

6	eggs	6
170 g	icing sugar, sifted	1½ cups
1 pkg	**oetker** vanilla sugar (9 g)	1 pkg
60 g	all-purpose flour, sifted	½ cup
90 g	hazelnuts, ground	1 cup
90 g	almonds, ground	1 cup
50 g	semi-sweet chocolate, shaved	2 squares

Filling:

500 mL	whipping cream	2 cups
1 pkg	**oetker** Whip it (10 g)	1 pkg
1 pkg	**oetker** vanilla sugar (9 g)	1 pkg
50 g	semi-sweet chocolate, shaved	2 squares

Decoration:

100 g	almonds, sliced, toasted	1 cup
50 g	milk chocolate, shaved	2 squares

PREHEAT oven to 180°C (350°F). Line a 25 cm (10") springform pan with waxed paper.
IN a mixing bowl, beat eggs until fluffy.
GRADUALLY beat in icing sugar and vanilla sugar.
IN another bowl, mix together flour, hazelnuts and almonds.
STIR into egg mixture.
FOLD chocolate into egg mixture, gently but thoroughly.

TURN mixture into prepared pan.
SMOOTH surface with a knife.
BAKE for 40-50 minutes.
LET cool.

USING a knife, loosen edges of torte.
CAREFULLY remove pan ring.

Filling:

IN a mixing bowl, beat whipping cream, Whip it and vanilla sugar to stiff peaks.
FOLD in chocolate.

SLICE torte twice to make three layers.
SPREAD one-quarter of the filling evenly over the bottom layer.
TOP with second layer.
SPREAD one-quarter of the filling evenly over second layer.
TOP with third layer.
SPREAD remaining filling over top and sides of torte.
DECORATE with almond slices and shaved chocolate.

Fruit Cream Torte

Fruchtcreme-Torte

Recipe No. 765

Ingredients:

48	lady fingers	48
125 mL	raspberry jam	½ cup
50 mL	orange liqueur	¼ cup

Filling:

250 mL	orange juice	1 cup
2	eggs	2
60 g	icing sugar, sifted	½ cup
1 pkg	**oetker** vanilla sugar (9 g)	1 pkg
1 pkg	gelatin (dissolved in 45 mL/3 tbsp hot water)	1 pkg
200 g	mascarpone cheese	1 cup
	juice of 1 lemon	
	pinch salt	pinch
250 mL	whipping cream	1 cup

Decoration:

250 mL	whipping cream	1 cup
1 pkg	**oetker** Whip it (10 g)	1 pkg
1 pkg	**oetker** vanilla sugar (9 g)	1 pkg
	some peach or orange sections	some
8	lady fingers	8

LINE a 25 cm (10") springform pan with waxed paper.
SPREAD jam on the top of all the lady fingers.
LINE bottom of pan with some lady fingers.
SPRINKLE with orange liqueur.

Filling:
IN a saucepan, combine orange juice, eggs, icing sugar and vanilla sugar.
HEAT to 80°C (175°F).
ADD gelatin to juice mixture. Stir well. Let cool.
WHEN mixture begins to set, add cheese, lemon juice and salt. Mix well.
IN mixing bowl, beat whipping cream to stiff peaks.
FOLD into cheese mixture, gently but thoroughly.
SPREAD a thin layer of filling over the lady fingers. Top with lady fingers.
CONTINUE this process until pan is full, ending with a layer of filling.
CHILL for 3 hours or overnight.
LOOSEN edges of torte with a knife.
REMOVE pan ring. Carefully remove waxed paper.
IN a mixing bowl, beat whipping cream, Whip it and vanilla sugar to stiff peaks.
DECORATE top and sides of torte with whipped cream, peach slices and lady fingers.

Potato Torte

Kartoffeltorte

Recipe No. 766

Batter:

3 medium	potatoes, parboiled, grated	3 medium
100 g	raisins	¾ cup
100 g	candied orange peel	¾ cup
15 mL	rum	1 tbsp
6	egg yolks	6
150 g	sugar	⅔ cup
1 pkg	**oetker** vanilla sugar (9 g)	1 pkg
150 g	hazelnuts, ground	1½ cups
6	egg whites	6

Dusting:

some	icing sugar, sifted	some

Batter:

PREHEAT oven to 180°C (350°F). Grease a 25 cm (10") springform pan. Sprinkle with bread crumbs.
PREPARE potatoes one day in advance. Cool completely.

SOAK raisins and candied orange peel in rum. LET stand overnight.

IN a mixing bowl, beat egg yolks, sugar and vanilla sugar until thick and fluffy.
ADD nuts, potatoes, raisins and orange peel. MIX well.

BEAT egg whites to stiff peaks. (Peaks should be so stiff that when a knife is inserted, the cut remains visible.)
FOLD beaten egg whites into potato mixture, gently but thoroughly.
TURN mixture into prepared pan.
SMOOTH surface with a knife.
BAKE for 60 minutes.
LET cool.

USING a knife, loosen edges of torte.
CAREFULLY remove pan ring.

PLACE a decorative stencil on top of the torte.
SPRINKLE with icing sugar to create a pattern on the surface of the torte.

Russian Torte

Tante Ernas Russische Torte

Recipe No. 767

Batter:

220 g	butter or margarine	1 cup
400 g	sugar	2 cups
4	egg yolks	4
250 mL	black tea, cold	1 cup
280 g	all-purpose flour, sifted	2 cups
240 g	walnuts, ground	2½ cups
4	egg whites	4

Filling:

110 g	butter, unsalted	½ cup
120 g	margarine	½ cup
120 g	icing sugar, sifted	1 cup
1 pkg	**oetker** vanilla sugar (9 g)	1 pkg
120 g	semi-sweet chocolate, softened	4 squares

Batter:

PREHEAT oven to 180°C (350°F). Grease a 25 cm (10") springform pan.

IN a mixing bowl, beat butter or margarine and sugar until fluffy. Add egg yolks, beating well after each addition.

GRADUALLY stir tea into butter mixture.

FOLD in flour and nuts, gently but thoroughly.

BEAT egg whites to stiff peaks. (Peaks should be so stiff that when a knife is inserted, the cut remains visible.)

FOLD beaten egg whites into butter mixture, gently but thoroughly.

TURN batter into prepared pan.

SMOOTH surface with a knife.

BAKE for 45-50 minutes. Let cool.

USING a knife, loosen edges of torte.

CAREFULLY remove pan ring.

Filling:

IN a mixing bowl, beat butter and margarine until fluffy. Gradually beat in icing sugar and vanilla sugar until smooth.

ADD chocolate. Mix well.

SLICE torte once to make two layers.

SPREAD two-thirds of the filling on the bottom layer.

ASSEMBLE torte.

SPREAD remaining filling over sides of torte.

DECORATE as desired.

35

Mozart Torte

Mozarttorte

Recipe No. 768

Batter:

150 g	butter	¾ cup
4	egg yolks	4
250 g	sugar	1¼ cups
2 pkgs	**oetker** vanilla sugar (18 g)	2 pkgs
10 mL	instant coffee	2 tsp
15 mL	rum	1 tbsp
	grated peel of 1 lemon OR	
½ btl	**oetker** lemon flavouring concentrate (1 mL)	½ btl
300 g	all-purpose flour, sifted	2½ cups
1 pkg	**oetker** baking powder (14 g)	1 pkg
30 mL	cocoa	2 tbsp
5 mL	instant coffee	1 tsp
250 mL	hot milk	1 cup
4	egg whites	4

Filling:

150 g	butter	¾ cup
100 g	icing sugar, sifted	¾ cup
1 pkg	**oetker** vanilla sugar (9 g)	1 pkg
60 g	chocolate, shaved	2 squares
30 mL	rum	2 tbsp

Brushing:

| 30 mL | red currant jam | 2 tbsp |

Decoration:

| | some chocolate sprinkles | some |

Batter:

PREHEAT oven to 180°C (350°F). Grease a 25 cm (10") springform pan.
IN a mixing bowl, beat butter until fluffy.
GRADUALLY beat in egg yolks, sugar, vanilla sugar, coffee, rum and lemon peel or flavouring concentrate.
IN another bowl, mix together flour, baking powder and cocoa.
SIFT over butter mixture.
DISSOLVE instant coffee in hot milk. Add to butter mixture, mix well.
BEAT egg whites to stiff peaks. (Peaks should be so stiff that when a knife is inserted, the cut remains visible.)
FOLD beaten egg whites into butter mixture, gently but thoroughly.

TURN batter into prepared pan.
SMOOTH surface with a knife.
BAKE for 50-60 minutes.
LET cool.

USING a knife, loosen edges of torte.
CAREFULLY remove pan ring.
CHILL overnight.

Filling:

IN a mixing bowl, beat butter until fluffy.
ADD icing sugar, vanilla sugar, chocolate and rum. Beat until smooth.

SLICE torte twice to make three layers.
SPREAD jam on the bottom layer.
TOP with second layer.
SPREAD one-third of the filling over top of the second layer. Assemble torte.
SPREAD remaining filling evenly over top and sides of torte.
DECORATE with chocolate sprinkles.

Chestnut Torte

Kastanientorte (Südsteirische)

Recipe No. 769

Batter:

2	egg yolks	2	
100 g	icing sugar, sifted	1	cup
1 pkg	**oetker** vanilla sugar (9 g)	1	pkg
30 g	hazelnuts, ground	⅓	cup
125 mL	chestnuts, strained or chestnut purée	½	cup
2	egg whites	2	
50 g	all-purpose flour	⅓	cup
1 pkg	**oetker** baking powder (14 g)	1	pkg

Filling:

55 g	butter	¼	cup
150 g	icing sugar, sifted	1½	cups
1 pkg	**oetker** vanilla sugar (9 g)	1	pkg
250 mL	chestnuts, strained or chestnut purée	1	cup
30 g	hazelnuts, ground	⅓	cup

Brushing:

75 mL	hot apricot jam	⅓	cup

Glaze:

80 g	butter	⅓	cup
100 g	semi-sweet chocolate	3½	squares
	OR		
1 pkg	**oetker** Chocofix (100 g)	1	pkg

Batter:

PREHEAT oven to 180°C (350°F). Grease and flour a 20 cm (8") springform pan.
IN a mixing bowl, beat egg yolks, icing sugar and vanilla sugar until thick and fluffy.
STIR in hazelnuts and chestnuts.
BEAT egg whites to stiff peaks. (Peaks should be so stiff that when a knife is inserted, the cut remains visible.)
SIFT flour and baking powder over the egg yolk mixture.
FOLD beaten egg whites, flour and baking powder into the egg yolk mixture, gently but thoroughly.

TURN mixture into prepared pan.
SMOOTH surface with a knife.
BAKE for 45-50 minutes.
LET cool.

Filling:

IN a mixing bowl, beat butter, icing sugar, vanilla sugar, chestnuts and hazelnuts until fluffy.

USING a knife, loosen edges of torte.
CAREFULLY remove pan ring.

SLICE torte twice to make three layers.
SPREAD filling over the surface of the bottom and middle layer. Assemble torte.
SPREAD jam over top of the torte.

Glaze:

IN a saucepan, combine butter and chocolate.
MELT slowly over low heat.
STIR until smooth.
GLAZE torte immediately.
CHILL overnight.

Cakes & Slices

Fruit and Nut Loaf

Apfelbrot

Recipe No. 770

Batter:

1½	kg	apples, cleaned, unpeeled, grated	5½ cups
500	g	figs or dried prunes, chopped	3½ cups
500	g	raisins	3½ cups
250	g	walnut halves	2 cups
250	g	sugar	1¼ cups
10	mL	cocoa	2 tsp
5	mL	cloves, ground	1 tsp
10	mL	cinnamon	2 tsp
10	mL	allspice	2 tsp
10	mL	rum	2 tsp
1	kg	all-purpose flour, sifted	6⅓ cups
2	pkgs	**oetker** baking powder (28 g)	2 pkgs

PREHEAT oven to 180°C (350°F). Grease two 23 x 13 x 7 cm (9 x 5 x 3") loaf pans.
IN a mixing bowl, combine apples, figs or prunes, raisins, walnuts, sugar, cocoa, spices and rum.
MIX thoroughly.
CHILL for 2-3 hours.

IN another bowl, mix together flour and baking powder.
ADD flour mixture to fruit mixture. Mix well.
TURN batter into prepared pans.
BAKE for 80 minutes.

Apple Bread

Dinkelkuchen

Recipe No. 771

Batter:

220	g	butter or margarine	1 cup
200	g	sugar	1 cup
1	pkg	**oetker** vanilla sugar (9 g)	1 pkg
	some	rum	some
4		egg yolks	4
250	g	all-purpose flour, sifted	1¾ cups
1	pkg	**oetker** baking powder (14 g)	1 pkg
120	g	hazelnuts, ground	1½ cups
15	mL	cocoa	1 tbsp
5	mL	cinnamon	1 tsp
4		egg whites	4
400	mL	sour apples, peeled, grated	1⅔ cups

PREHEAT oven to 180°C (350°F). Grease a 23 x 13 x 7 cm (9 x 5 x 3") loaf pan.
IN a mixing bowl, beat butter or margarine until fluffy.
GRADUALLY beat in sugar, vanilla sugar, rum and egg yolks.
IN another bowl, combine flour, baking powder, hazelnuts, cocoa and cinnamon. Mix well.
FOLD flour mixture into butter mixture, gently but thoroughly.

BEAT egg whites to stiff peaks. (Peaks should be so stiff that when a knife is inserted, the cut remains visible.)
FOLD beaten egg whites and apples into the butter mixture.

TURN batter into prepared pan.
SMOOTH surface with a knife.
BAKE for 70 minutes.
COOL completely in pan.
TURN cake onto a serving platter.

Royal Banana Cake

Königliches Bananenbiskuit

Recipe No. 772

Batter:

8	egg whites	8
300 g	sugar	1½ cups
6	egg yolks	6
1 pkg	**oetker** vanilla sugar (9 g)	1 pkg
200 g	all-purpose flour	1½ cups

Sprinkling:

1 shot	Cointreau	1 shot

Brushing and Topping:

50 mL	apricot jam	¼ cup
6	bananas, sliced	6

Topping:

1 pkg	**oetker** vanilla pudding (43 g)	1 pkg
250 mL	milk	1 cup
45 mL	sugar (first amount)	3 tbsp
2	egg yolks	2
100 g	sugar (second amount)	½ cup
1 pkg	**oetker** vanilla sugar (9 g)	1 pkg
220 g	butter, softened	1 cup

Glaze:

2 pkgs	**oetker** Chocofix (200 g)	2 pkgs

Batter:
PREHEAT oven to 180°C (350°F). Line a 40 x 25 x 2 cm (15½ x 10½ x ¾") baking sheet with parchment paper.
BEAT egg whites to soft peaks. Gradually beat in sugar until stiff peaks form. (Peaks should be so stiff that when a knife is inserted, the cut remains visible.)
IN another bowl, combine egg yolks and vanilla sugar. Beat until thick and fluffy.
FOLD egg yolk mixture into egg white mixture gently but thoroughly.
SIFT flour over egg mixture. Mix well.

SPREAD batter 1 cm (⅜") thick in prepared baking sheet.
BAKE for 15-20 minutes.

AFTER baking, turn cake onto a tea towel sprinkled generously with icing sugar.
BRUSH parchment paper with cold water.
REMOVE carefully but quickly. Let cake cool completely.

SPRINKLE surface of cake with Cointreau.
SPREAD jam evenly over cake.
TOP with sliced bananas.

Filling:
PREPARE pudding according to package directions, using only 250 mL (1 cup) of milk and 45 mL (3 tbsp) of sugar.
COVER surface of pudding with saran wrap to prevent skin from forming.
COOL completely, stirring occasionally.
FOLD in egg yolks, sugar (second amount), vanilla sugar and one-half of the butter, gently but thoroughly.

IN a mixing bowl, beat remaining butter until fluffy.
BEAT in pudding mixture, one spoonful at a time.
USING a warm knife, spread filling evenly over the bananas.

Glaze:
PREPARE Chocofix according to package directions.
GLAZE cake.

Danube Delights

Donauwellen

Recipe No. 773

Batter:

220 g	butter	2 cups
260 g	sugar	1¼ cups
1 pkg	**oetker** vanilla sugar (9 g)	1 pkg
6	eggs	6
350 g	all-purpose flour	2½ cups
1 pkg	**oetker** baking powder (14 g)	1 pkg
30 mL	cocoa	2 tbsp
1 L	sour cherries, drained, pitted	4 cups

Topping:

1 pkg	**oetker** vanilla pudding (43 g)	1 pkg
500 mL	milk	2 cups
100 g	sugar	½ cup
220 g	butter, unsalted	2 cups
5 drops	**oetker** lemon flavouring concentrate	5 drops

Glaze:

| 2 pkgs | **oetker** Chocofix | 2 pkgs |

Batter:

PREHEAT oven to 175°C (350°F). Grease and flour a 40 x 25 x 2 cm (15½ x 10½ x ¾") baking sheet.
IN a mixing bowl, beat butter until fluffy.
GRADUALLY beat in sugar, vanilla sugar and eggs.
SIFT flour and baking powder over the butter mixture. Fold in gently but thoroughly.
DIVIDE batter in half.
ADD cocoa to one-half of the batter.

TURN light batter into prepared baking sheet.
SPREAD dark batter evenly over light batter.
SMOOTH surface with a knife.
TOP evenly with cherries.
BAKE for 30 minutes.
AFTER baking, cool completely.

Topping:

IN a mixing bowl, combine pudding, 125 mL (½ cup) of the pre-measured milk and sugar.
STIR until smooth.
IN a saucepan, bring remaining milk to a boil.
ADD pudding mixture to milk. Bring to a boil while stirring constantly.
REMOVE from heat. Cover surface of pudding with saran wrap to prevent skin from forming.
COOL completely, stirring occasionally.

IN another bowl, beat butter until fluffy.
ADD lemon flavouring concentrate.
STIRRING constantly, add pudding mixture to butter mixture one spoonful at a time.
SPREAD filling evenly over cake.
REFRIGERATE.

Glaze:

PREPARE Chocofix according to package directions.
GLAZE cake.

47

*B*uttermilk Cake

*B*uttermilchkuchen

Recipe No. 774

Batter:

220 g	butter, softened	2 cups
500 g	icing sugar, sifted	4⅓ cups
1 pkg	**oetker** vanilla sugar (9 g)	1 pkg
4	egg yolks	4
170 g	semi-sweet chocolate, softened	6 squares
500 g	all-purpose flour	3½ cups
1 pkg	**oetker** baking powder (14 g)	1 pkg
250 mL	buttermilk	1 cup
4	egg whites	4

Sprinkling:

some	icing sugar, sifted	some

Batter:

PREHEAT *oven to 180°C (350°F). Grease and flour a 33 x 23 x 5 cm (13 x 9 x 2") cake pan.*

IN *a mixing bowl, beat butter until fluffy.*

GRADUALLY *beat in icing sugar, vanilla sugar, egg yolks and chocolate.*

SIFT *together flour and baking powder. Stir into butter mixture alternately with buttermilk.*

BEAT *egg whites to stiff peaks. (Peaks should be so stiff that when a knife is inserted, the cut remains visible.)*

FOLD *beaten egg whites into butter mixture, gently but thoroughly.*

TURN *batter into prepared cake pan.*

BAKE *for 50 minutes.*

COOL *completely.*

DECORATE *cake with icing sugar.*

CUT *into squares.*

Sour Cream Cake

Becherkuchen

Recipe No. 775

Batter:

250 mL	sour cream	1 cup
150 g	all-purpose flour, sifted	1¼ cups
½ pkg	**oetker** baking powder (7 g)	½ pkg
200 g	sugar	1 cup
50 g	cocoa, sifted	¾ cup
120 g	hazelnuts, ground	1 cup
125 mL	vegetable oil	½ cup
4	eggs	4

Sprinkling:

some	icing sugar, sifted	some

Batter:

GREASE a 25 cm (10") springform pan.
IN a mixing bowl, combine sour cream, flour, baking powder, sugar, cocoa, hazelnuts, oil and eggs. Mix well.

TURN batter into prepared pan.
SMOOTH surface with a knife.
PLACE on middle oven rack in <u>cold</u> oven.
BAKE at 180°C (350°F) for 40-50 minutes.
LET cake cool in pan.

TURN cake onto serving platter.
DUST with icing sugar.

49

Calafatti Slices

Calafatti-Schnitten

Recipe No. 776

Dough:

400 g	all-purpose flour	3 cups	
120 g	icing sugar, sifted	1 cup	
1 pkg	**oetker** vanilla sugar (9 g)	1 pkg	
pinch	cinnamon	pinch	
120 g	nuts, finely ground	1 cup	
5	egg yolks	5	
220 g	cold butter	1 cup	

Brushing and Sprinkling:

15 mL	rum	1 tbsp	
375 mL	red currant or cranberry jam	1½ cups	

Topping:

5	egg whites	5	
120 g	sugar	½ cup	
200 g	nuts, finely ground	2 cups	
90 g	semi-sweet chocolate, shaved	3 squares	

Dough:

PREHEAT oven to 180°C (350°F). Lightly grease a 40 x 25 x 2 cm (15½ x 10½ x ¾") baking sheet.

SIFT flour onto a working surface.

MAKE a well in the centre.

PUT icing sugar, vanilla sugar, cinnamon, nuts and egg yolks into the well.

CUT butter in small pieces over the ingredients in the well.

COVER with flour.

STARTING from the centre, work all ingredients into a smooth dough.

CHILL for 30 minutes.

ROLL dough 3 mm (⅛") thick. Press into prepared baking sheet.

USING a fork, prick dough several times.

BAKE for 10 minutes.

SPRINKLE rum over surface of cake.

TOP with jam.

Topping:

PREHEAT oven to 170°C (350°F).

IN a mixing bowl, beat egg whites to soft peaks. Gradually beat in sugar until stiff peaks form. (Peaks should be so stiff that when a knife is inserted, the cut remains visible.)

FOLD in nuts and chocolate, gently but thoroughly.

SPREAD mixture evenly over jam.

BAKE for 15-20 minutes. Cool completely.

CUT into slices.

*F*ruit Cream Cake

*F*ruchtrahmkuchen

Recipe No. 777

Dough:

120 g	all-purpose flour	¾	cup
pinch	**oetker** baking powder		pinch
45 mL	sugar	3	tbsp
½ pkg	**oetker** vanilla sugar (4.5 g)	½	pkg
pinch	cinnamon		pinch
	grated peel of 1 lemon		
1	egg yolk	1	
80 g	cold butter	⅓	cup

Filling:

3	egg whites	3	
1 pkg	**oetker** vanilla sugar (9 g)	1	pkg
55 g	butter	¼	cup
80 g	all-purpose flour	½	cup
80 g	sugar	⅓	cup
750 mL	whipping cream	3	cups
2	egg yolks	2	

Topping:

875 mL	stewed cherries, drained, pitted	3½	cups

Sprinkling:

some	icing sugar, sifted		some

Dough:

GREASE a 33 x 23 x 5 cm (13 x 9 x 2") cake pan.

SIFT flour and baking powder onto a working surface.

MAKE a well in the centre. Put sugar, vanilla sugar, cinnamon, lemon peel and egg yolk in the well.

CUT butter in small pieces over the ingredients in the well.

COVER with flour.

STARTING from the centre work all ingredients into a smooth dough.

CHILL for 30 minutes.

PREHEAT oven to 180°C (350°F).

ROLL dough 3 mm (⅛") thick. Press into prepared cake pan.

BAKE for 6-8 minutes. Let cool in pan.

Filling:

PREHEAT oven to 160°C (325°F).

IN a mixing bowl, beat egg whites to stiff peaks. Gradually beat in vanilla sugar. (Peaks should be so stiff that when a knife is inserted, the cut remains visible.) Set aside.

IN a saucepan, heat butter. Add flour. Cook for 1-2 minutes.

STIR in sugar.

SLOWLY add whipping cream. Bring to a boil. (Reduce mixture by boiling 2-3 minutes.)

REMOVE from heat.

STIR in egg yolks and beaten egg whites.

TOP cake evenly with cherries.

SPREAD filling over cherries.

BAKE for 70-80 minutes.

USING a knife, loosen and carefully remove the warm cake from the pan. Cut into slices.

DUST surface of cake with icing sugar.

SUGGESTION: Fruit Cream Cake tastes best served warm.

Cream of Wheat Slices

Grießschnitten

Recipe No. 778

Dough:

650 g	all-purpose flour	3⅓	cups
200 g	icing sugar, sifted	1⅔	cups
2 pkgs	**oetker** vanilla sugar (18 g)	2	pkgs
100 mL	honey	⅓	cup
15 mL	cocoa	1	tbsp
15 mL	baking soda	1	tbsp
3	eggs	3	
220 g	cold butter	1	cup

Filling:

1 L	milk	4	cups
120 g	cream of wheat	½	cup
1 pkg	**oetker** vanilla sugar (9 g)	1	pkg
300 g	butter	1½	cups
200 g	icing sugar, sifted	1⅔	cups
45 mL	rum	3	tbsp

Spreading:

15 mL	honey	1	tbsp
5 mL	lemon juice	1	tsp

Dough:

GREASE and flour a 33 x 23 x 5 cm (13 x 9 x 2") cake pan.
SIFT flour onto a working surface.
MAKE a well in the centre. Put icing sugar, vanilla sugar, honey, cocoa, baking soda and eggs in the well.
CUT butter in small pieces over ingredients in the well.
COVER with flour.
STARTING at the centre, work all ingredients into a smooth dough.
CHILL for 30 minutes.

PREHEAT oven to 180°C (350°F).
DIVIDE the dough into five equal parts.
ROLL out each portion of dough into a 33 x 23 cm (13 x 9") rectangle.
PLACE dough rectangle in prepared cake pan.
BAKE individually for 10-13 minutes.
REPEAT baking process four times.

Filling:

IN a saucepan, heat milk.
STIR in cream of wheat and vanilla sugar.
BRING to a boil.
REMOVE from heat. Cool completely.
IN a mixing bowl, beat butter, icing sugar and rum until fluffy (at least 10 minutes).
ADD cream of wheat mixture, one spoonful at a time, beating well after each addition.

SPREAD filling evenly over one layer. Smooth surface with a knife.
TOP with second layer.
REPEAT this process, ending with a cake layer.
CHILL overnight.

Spreading:

IN a saucepan, combine honey and lemon juice. Heat slightly.
SPREAD honey mixture evenly over top of cake.
BEFORE serving, cut into pieces.

Coconut-Quark Cake

Kokos-Bienenstich mit Topfenfüllung

Recipe No. 779

Dough:

220 g	all-purpose flour	1½ cups	
1 pkg	**oetker** instant dry yeast (7 g)	1 pkg	
30 mL	sugar	2 tbsp	
1 pkg	**oetker** vanilla sugar (9 g)	1 pkg	
5 drops	**oetker** lemon flavouring concentrate	5 drops	
1	egg	1	
45 mL	butter, melted	3 tbsp	
75 mL	lukewarm milk	⅓ cup	

Topping:

75 g	butter or margarine	⅓ cup	
75 g	sugar	⅓ cup	
15 mL	honey	1 tbsp	
100 g	coconut, shredded	1⅓ cups	
45 mL	milk	3 tbsp	

Filling:

1 pkg	**oetker** vanilla pudding (43 g)	1 pkg	
500 mL	milk	2 cups	
45 mL	sugar	3 tbsp	
2 cans	pineapple pieces (2 x 540 mL)	2 cans	
½ pkg	gelatin	½ pkg	
250 g	quark or cream cheese	1 cup	

Dough:

GREASE a 25 cm (10") springform pan.
SPRINKLE with bread crumbs.
SIFT flour into a mixing bowl.
ADD yeast and mix well.
MAKE a well in the centre. Put sugar, vanilla sugar, flavouring concentrate, egg, butter and milk in the well.
KNEAD dough with an electric mixer fitted with dough hooks on high speed until dough is smooth, blistery and no longer sticky.
COVER. Let rest in a warm place until doubled in size.

Topping:

IN a saucepan, combine butter or margarine, sugar and honey. Heat until melted.
ADD coconut. Stir constantly. Cook mixture until coconut is golden yellow.
REMOVE from heat.
ADD milk. Return to heat. Continue cooking on low until sugar has completely dissolved.
REMOVE from heat. Cool completely.

KNEAD dough. Press into bottom of springform pan.
SPREAD topping evenly over dough.
COVER. Let rest in a warm place for 20 minutes.
PREHEAT oven to 200°C (400°F).
BAKE on middle oven rack for 20-30 minutes.
COOL completely.

Filling:

PREPARE pudding according to package directions using milk and sugar quantities indicated in the recipe. Cool completely.
DRAIN pineapple. Reserve juice.
DISSOLVE gelatin in 45 mL (3 tbsp) of "warm" pineapple juice.
FOLD gelatin, quark or cream cheese and pineapple pieces into the pudding mixture, gently but thoroughly.

SLICE cake once to make two layers.
SPREAD filling evenly over bottom layer.
SMOOTH surface with a knife. Cover with top layer.
CHILL for 3-4 hours.

Pumpkin Seed Cake

Kürbiskernkuchen

Recipe No. 780

Batter:

170 g	margarine	¾ cup
200 g	sugar	1 cup
2 pkgs	**oetker** vanilla sugar (18 g)	2 pkgs
2	eggs	2
3 drops	**oetker** almond flavouring concentrate	3 drops
250 g	quark	1 cup
300 g	all-purpose flour	2 cups
1 pkg	**oetker** baking powder (14 g)	1 pkg
200 g	pumpkin seeds or almonds, ground	2 cups

Batter:

GREASE a 23 x 13 x 7 cm (9 x 5 x 3") loaf pan.
IN a mixing bowl, beat margarine until fluffy.
GRADUALLY beat in sugar, vanilla sugar, eggs and flavouring concentrate.
FOLD quark into egg mixture, gently but thoroughly.
SIFT flour and baking powder into a mixing bowl.
STIR in pumpkin seeds or almonds.
ADD flour mixture to quark mixture.
STIR until smooth.

TURN batter into prepared loaf pan.
PLACE pan on lower oven rack in a <u>cold</u> oven.
BAKE at 180°C (350°F) for 60 minutes.

*P*lum Slices

Pflaumenschnitten

Recipe No. 781

Batter:

300 g	marzipan	10	oz
300 g	sugar	1½	cups
300 g	butter or	1⅓	cups
	margarine, softened		
	grated peel of 1 lemon		
	OR		
½ btl	**oetker** lemon flavouring	½	btl
	concentrate (1 mL)		
10 mL	cinnamon	2	tsp
5	eggs	5	
300 g	wholewheat flour	2	cups
300 g	almonds, ground	3	cups

Topping:

650 g	plums, pitted, halved	1½	lb

Glaze:

1 pkg	**oetker** instant	1	pkg
	clear glaze (30 g)		

Batter:

PREHEAT oven to 180°C (350°F). Grease a 40 x 25 x 2 cm (15½ x 10½ x ¾") baking sheet. (If baking sheet has no rim, fold a piece of foil in place to prevent expanding dough from spilling in oven.)

ON a working surface, knead marzipan with sugar and butter or margarine.

ADD lemon peel or flavouring concentrate and cinnamon. Knead well.

PLACE mixture in a mixing bowl.

ADD eggs. Using an electric mixer, beat well.

GRADUALLY add flour and almonds. Stir.

SPREAD batter in prepared baking sheet.
SMOOTH surface with a knife.

USING a knife, make two small incisions in the plums lengthwise.

COVER dough completely with plum halves (cut side face up).

BAKE for 60 minutes.

COOL completely.

PREPARE glaze according to package directions.

GLAZE cake. Cut into slices.

Suggestion: *Substitute plums with apricot halves.*

Lambada Slices

Lambada-Schnitten

Recipe No. 782

Batter:

4	eggs	4
260 g	sugar	1¼ cups
1 pkg	**oetker** vanilla sugar (9 g)	1 pkg
125 mL	vegetable oil	½ cup
125 mL	milk	½ cup
300 g	all-purpose flour, sifted	2¼ cups
½ pkg	**oetker** baking powder (7 g)	½ pkg

Topping:

1 pkg	**oetker** vanilla pudding (43 g)	1 pkg
500 mL	orange juice (first amount)	2 cups
45 mL	sugar	3 tbsp
250 mL	whipping cream	1 cup
½ pkg	gelatin (dissolved in 30 mL/2 tbsp hot water)	½ pkg
250 mL	orange juice (second amount)	1 cup
30 mL	rum	2 tbsp
36-40	lady fingers	36-40

Glaze:

1-2 pkgs	**oetker** Chocofix (100 g)	1-2 pkgs

Batter:
PREHEAT oven to 200°C (400°F). Grease a 40 x 25 x 2 cm (15½ x 10½ x ¾") baking sheet.
IN a mixing bowl, beat eggs, sugar and vanilla sugar.
ADD vegetable oil and milk. Mix well.
MIX together flour and baking powder.
ADD to egg mixture. Stir until smooth.

TURN batter into prepared baking sheet.
BAKE for 10-15 minutes.
COOL completely before removing from sheet.

Topping:
PREPARE pudding according to package directions, using orange juice (first amount) in place of milk and sugar as indicated in recipe.
LET pudding cool. (Place saran wrap over the surface of the pudding to prevent skin from forming.)
SPREAD pudding evenly over cake.

BEAT whipping cream to stiff peaks.
FOLD in gelatin, gently but thoroughly.
SPREAD gelatin mixture evenly over pudding mixture.

IN a large mixing bowl, combine orange juice (second amount) and rum.
SOAK lady fingers in orange mixture. Toss gently.
TOP cake with lady fingers.

Glaze:
PREPARE Chocofix according to package directions.
DRIZZLE glaze over lady fingers. Let cool.
CUT into slices.

Hippos

Nilpferde

Recipe No. 783

Ingredients:

170 g	butter, softened	¾ cup
240 g	icing sugar, sifted	2 cups
1 pkg	**oetker** vanilla sugar (9 g)	1 pkg
6	egg yolks	6
90 g	all-purpose flour, sifted	¾ cup
170 g	semi-sweet chocolate, softened	6 squares
120 g	hazelnuts, finely ground	1½ cups
4	egg whites	4

Topping:

300 g	butter	1⅓ cups
400 g	icing sugar, sifted	3½ cups
2 pkgs	**oetker** vanilla sugar (18 g)	2 pkgs
125 mL	lukewarm cocoa (dissolve 10 mL/2 tsp of cocoa in 125 mL/ ½ cup hot milk)	½ cup
125 mL	rum	½ cup
300 g	coconut, shredded	3½ cups

GREASE a 33 x 23 x 5 cm (13 x 9 x 2") cake pan.
IN a mixing bowl, beat butter, icing sugar, vanilla sugar and egg yolks until fluffy.
IN another bowl, mix together flour, chocolate and hazelnuts.
ADD to butter mixture, one spoonful at a time, stirring well after each addition.

BEAT egg whites to stiff peaks. (Peaks should be so stiff that when a knife is inserted, the cut remains visible.)
FOLD beaten egg whites into butter mixture, gently but thoroughly.

SPREAD mixture in prepared cake pan.
PLACE on middle oven rack in <u>cold</u> oven.
BAKE at 190°C (375°F) for 25-30 minutes.
REMOVE cake from pan.
COOL completely.

Topping:
IN a mixing bowl, beat butter, icing sugar and vanilla sugar.
ADD cocoa and rum. Mix well
STIR in coconut.

PLACE butter mixture in a pastry bag fitted with a large plain tube.
PIPE mixture on the surface of the cake.
USING a sharp, hot knife, cut cake into rectangles.

Guglhupf Cake

Obersguglhupf

Recipe No. 784

Batter:

4	eggs	4
170 g	sugar	¾ cup
1 pkg	**oetker** vanilla sugar (9 g)	1 pkg
5 drops	**oetker** lemon flavouring concentrate	5 drops
220 g	all-purpose flour, sifted	1½ cups
½ pkg	**oetker** baking powder (7 g)	½ pkg
250 mL	whipping cream	1 cup

Batter:

PREHEAT oven to 170°C (350°F). Grease a bundt pan. Sprinkle with bread crumbs.

IN a mixing bowl, beat eggs, sugar, vanilla sugar and flavouring concentrate until thick and fluffy.

MIX together flour and baking powder.

ADD flour mixture to egg mixture, one spoonful at a time, stirring well after each addition.

IN another bowl, beat whipping cream to stiff peaks.

FOLD whipped cream into egg mixture, gently but thoroughly.

TURN batter into prepared pan.
SMOOTH surface with a knife.
BAKE for 35-40 minutes.
DUST with icing sugar.

Mexican Apple Cake

Mexikanischer Apfelkuchen

Recipe No. 785

100 g	rolled oats	1 cup
Batter:		
150 g	butter	⅔ cup
120 g	sugar	½ cup
3	eggs	3
50 g	all-purpose flour, sifted	⅓ cup
1 pkg	**oetker** baking powder (14 g)	1 pkg
Filling:		
8 medium	apples, peeled and sliced	8 medium
	juice of ½ lemon	
45 mL	butter, melted	3 tbsp
60 g	sugar	¼ cup
1 pkg	**oetker** vanilla sugar (9 g)	1 pkg
75 g	almonds, sliced	1 cup

PREHEAT oven to 160°C (325°F). Grease a 23 cm (9″) springform pan. Sprinkle with rolled oats.

Batter:
IN a mixing bowl, beat butter until fluffy.
GRADUALLY beat in sugar and eggs.
MIX together flour and baking powder.
FOLD into egg mixture, gently but thoroughly.
TURN two-thirds of the batter into prepared pan.

Filling:
IN a double boiler, heat apples in lemon juice until soft. Cool completely.
FOLD in butter, sugar, vanilla sugar and almonds. Mix well.
SPREAD apple mixture over batter in pan.
USING a teaspoon, scoop out small portions of remaining batter and place on top of apple mixture.

BAKE for 60 minutes.

USING a knife, loosen edges of cake.
CAREFULLY remove pan ring.

Poetry Cake

Poesie-Kuchen

Recipe No. 786

Batter:

300 g	butter	1⅓ cups	
150 g	sugar	¾ cup	
15 mL	honey	1 tbsp	
2 pkgs	**oetker** vanilla sugar (18 g)	2 pkgs	
½ btl	**oetker** lemon flavouring concentrate (1 mL)	½ btl	
6	egg whites	6	
90 g	all-purpose flour	½ cup	
	pinch **oetker** baking powder	pinch	
90 g	hazelnuts, ground	1 cup	

Glaze:

75 mL	evaporated milk	⅓ cup	
30 mL	butter or margarine	2 tbsp	
180 g	sugar	¾ cup	
1 pkg	**oetker** vanilla sugar (9 g)	1 pkg	

Decoration:

1 pkg	**oetker** Chocofix (100 g)	1 pkg	

Batter:

PREHEAT oven to 180°C (350°F). Grease and flour a 33 x 23 x 5 cm (13 x 9 x 2") cake pan.
IN a mixing bowl, beat butter, sugar, honey, vanilla sugar and flavouring concentrate until fluffy.
BEAT egg whites to stiff peaks. (Peaks should be so stiff that when a knife is inserted, the cut remains visible.)
FOLD beaten egg whites into butter mixture, one spoonful at a time.
SIFT flour and baking powder over the butter mixture. Mix well.
FOLD in hazelnuts, gently but thoroughly.
TURN batter into prepared pan.
BAKE for 20-25 minutes.

Glaze:

IN a small saucepan, combine evaporated milk, butter or margarine and sugar.
COOK on low heat for 30 minutes, stirring occasionally.
REMOVE from heat. Stir in vanilla sugar.
BEAT with electric mixer at medium speed until mixture starts to thicken.
GLAZE the still warm cake. Spread quickly with a wet knife.

Decoration:

PREPARE Chocofix according to package directions. Decorate cake as desired.

Chocolate Slices

Palffy-Schnitten

Recipe No. 787

Ingredients:

180 g	butter, softened	¾	cup
4	egg yolks	4	
170 g	sugar	¾	cup
170 g	semi-sweet chocolate, softened	6	squares
4	egg whites	4	
45 mL	all-purpose flour, sifted	3	tbsp

Sprinkling:

chocolate, shaved

PREHEAT oven to 190°C (375°F). Grease and flour a 33 x 23 x 5 cm (13 x 9 x 2") cake pan.

IN a mixing bowl, beat butter, egg yolks, sugar and chocolate until fluffy.

IN another bowl, beat egg whites to stiff peaks. (Peaks should be so stiff that when a knife is inserted, the cut remains visible.)
FOLD beaten egg whites into butter mixture, gently but thoroughly.

ADD flour to one-third of the butter mixture.
MIX well.
SPREAD mixture evenly in prepared pan.
BAKE for 10-12 minutes.
COOL completely.

SPREAD remaining two-thirds butter mixture evenly over cake.
SPRINKLE with chocolate.

CUT into pieces. Serve chilled.

*R*um Wreath

*R*umkranz

Recipe No. 788

Batter:

220 g	butter	2 cups	
250 g	icing sugar, sifted	2 cups	
1 pkg	**oetker** vanilla sugar (9 g)	1 pkg	
½ btl	**oetker** rum flavouring concentrate (1mL)	½ btl	
4	eggs	4	
220 g	all-purpose flour	1½ cups	
½ pkg	**oetker** baking powder (7 g)	½ pkg	
200 g	semi-sweet chocolate, coarsely chopped	7 squares	

Glaze:

125 mL	rum	½ cup	
150 g	icing sugar, sifted	1½ cups	

Batter:
GREASE a 23 x 10 cm (9 x 4") tube pan.
IN a mixing bowl, beat butter, icing sugar, vanilla sugar and flavouring concentrate until fluffy.
ADD eggs, one at a time, stirring well after each addition.
IN another bowl, mix together flour and baking powder.
SIFT over butter mixture.
FOLD in chocolate, gently but thoroughly.

TURN batter into prepared pan.
PLACE on middle oven rack in <u>cold</u> oven.
BAKE at 200°C (400°F) for 30-35 minutes.

AFTER baking, immediately turn cake onto a wire cooling rack.

Glaze:
IN a saucepan, combine rum and icing sugar.
BRING to a quick boil.
REMOVE from heat.
POUR warm rum mixture over cake.

Wobble Cake

Schüttelkuchen

Recipe No. 789

Batter:

300 g	all-purpose flour, sifted	2¼ cups	
½ pkg	**oetker** baking powder (7 g)	½ pkg	
250 g	icing sugar, sifted	2 cups	
1 pkg	**oetker** vanilla sugar (9 g)	1 pkg	
180 g	hazelnuts, ground	1½ cups	
250 mL	cold coffee	1 cup	
4	eggs	4	
180 g	butter, melted	¾ cup	

Brushing:

175 mL	red currant or apricot jam	¾ cup	
15 mL	liqueur	1 tbsp	

Glaze:

1 pkg	**oetker** Chocofix (100 g)	1 pkg	

Batter:

GREASE a 40 x 25 x 2 cm (15½ x 10½ x ¾")
baking sheet. (If baking sheet has no rim, fold
a piece of foil in place to prevent expanding
dough from spilling in oven.)
SIFT flour and baking powder into a mixing
bowl.
ADD icing sugar, vanilla sugar and hazelnuts.
MIX well.
IN another bowl, combine coffee, eggs and
butter. Stir.
ADD coffee mixture to flour mixture.
USING an electric mixer, beat well.

TURN batter into prepared baking sheet.
PLACE sheet on middle oven rack in <u>cold</u>
oven.
BAKE at 180°C (350°F) for 25-30 minutes.
COOL completely.

MIX together jam and liqueur.
SPREAD evenly over cake.

Glaze:
PREPARE glaze according to package
directions.
GLAZE cake.

Rum Cake

Rumkuchen

Recipe No. 790

Batter:

5	egg yolks	5
200 g	sugar	1 cup
150 g	all-purpose flour, sifted	1¼ cups
½ pkg	**oetker** baking powder (7 g)	½ pkg
150 g	nuts, ground	1½ cups
125 mL	milk	½ cup
5	egg whites	5

Topping:

125 mL	water	½ cup
125 mL	rum	½ cup
	OR	
2 btls	**oetker** rum flavouring concentrate (4 mL)	2 btls
100 g	sugar	½ cup

Glaze:

1 pkg	**oetker** Chocofix (100 g)	1 pkg

Decoration:

250 mL	whipping cream	1 cup
5 mL	**oetker** vanilla sugar	1 tsp
1 pkg	**oetker** Whip it (10 g)	1 pkg

Batter:

PREHEAT oven to 190°C (375°F). Grease and flour a 23 x 13 x 7 cm (9 x 5 x 3") loaf pan.

IN a mixing bowl, beat egg yolks and sugar until thick and fluffy.

IN another bowl, mix together flour and baking powder.

STIR flour mixture into egg yolk mixture.

FOLD in nuts and milk, gently but thoroughly.

BEAT egg whites to stiff peaks. (Peaks should be so stiff that when a knife is inserted, the cut remains visible.)

FOLD beaten egg whites into egg yolk mixture gently but thoroughly.

TURN batter into prepared pan.

SMOOTH surface with a knife.

BAKE for 45-55 minutes.

Topping:

IN a saucepan, bring water to a boil.

ADD rum or flavouring concentrate and sugar. Stir until mixture is smooth.

REMOVE from heat.

USING a knife, loosen edges of hot cake carefully from pan. Turn onto a serving platter.

POUR rum mixture over cake immediately.

COVER. Let stand overnight.

Glaze:

PREPARE Chocofix according to package directions.

GLAZE cake.

Decoration:

IN a mixing bowl, beat whipping cream, vanilla sugar and Whip it to stiff peaks.

PLACE whipped cream mixture in a pastry bag fitted with a small round tube.

DECORATE cake.

71

Grape Pie

Traubenkuchen

Recipe No. 791

Dough:

200 g	all-purpose flour	1½ cups
50 g	icing sugar, sifted	½ cup
1 pkg	**oetker** vanilla sugar (9 g)	1 pkg
pinch	salt	pinch
1	egg	1
110 g	cold butter	½ cup

Topping:

750 mL	grapes	3 cups
175 mL	yogurt	¾ cup
100 g	sugar	½ cup
2 pkgs	**oetker** vanilla sugar (18 g)	2 pkgs
50 mL	cream cheese, softened	¼ cup
	grated peel of 1 lemon	
3	eggs	3
50 g	all-purpose flour, sifted	⅓ cup

Dough:

GREASE a pie or quiche plate.
SIFT flour onto a working surface.
MAKE a well in the centre. Put icing sugar, vanilla sugar, salt and egg in the well.
CUT butter in small pieces over the ingredients in the well.
COVER with flour.
STARTING from the centre, work all ingredients into a smooth dough.
CHILL for one hour.

ROLL out dough ½ cm (³/₁₆") thick. Line prepared pan with dough.
CHILL for 30 minutes.

PREHEAT oven to 190°C (375°F).

Topping:

WASH and drain grapes. Set aside.
IN a mixing bowl, combine yogurt, sugar, vanilla sugar, cream cheese and lemon peel.
STIR until smooth.
ADD eggs, one at a time, beating well after each addition.
FOLD in flour and one-third of the grapes.

SPREAD yogurt mixture evenly over dough.
SMOOTH surface with a knife.
TOP with remaining grapes.
BAKE for 30-40 minutes.
COOL completely.

73

Christmas Bread

Weihnachtsbrot

Recipe No. 792

Batter:

60 g	butter	¼ cup
180 g	icing sugar, sifted	1½ cups
3	egg yolks	3
1 pkg	**oetker** vanilla sugar (9 g)	1 pkg
30 mL	milk	2 tbsp
30 mL	rum	2 tbsp
	grated peel of ½ lemon	
	juice of ½ lemon	
200 g	all-purpose flour	1½ cups
½ pkg	**oetker** baking powder (7 g)	½ pkg
100 g	candied orange peel, finely chopped	⅔ cup
50 g	candied lemon peel, finely chopped	⅓ cup
90 g	semi-sweet chocolate, coarsely chopped	3-4 squares
50 g	hazelnuts, ground	½ cup
50 g	walnuts, coarsely chopped	½ cup
100 g	raisins	¾ cup
50 g	pine nuts	⅓ cup
3	egg whites	3

Sprinkling:

10 mL	rum	2 tsp

Batter:

PREHEAT oven to 180°C (350°F). Grease a 23 x 13 x 7 cm (9 x 5 x 3") loaf pan.

IN a mixing bowl, beat butter, icing sugar, egg yolks and vanilla sugar until fluffy.

ADD milk, rum, lemon peel and lemon juice. MIX well.

SIFT flour and baking powder over the butter mixture. Fold in gently but thoroughly.

ADD candied orange and lemon peel, chocolate, hazelnuts, walnuts, raisins and pine nuts.

BEAT egg whites to stiff peaks. (Peaks should be so stiff that when a knife is inserted, the cut remains visible.)

FOLD beaten egg whites into butter mixture gently but thoroughly.

TURN batter into prepared pan.

BAKE for approximately 60 minutes.

LET bread cool in pan for a few minutes.

TURN onto a piece of aluminum foil.

SPRINKLE with rum.

WRAP cake in foil. Leave for 2-3 days before cutting.

Cookies & More

*P*easant Rounds

*B*auernbrötchen

Recipe No. 793

Ingredients:

3	egg yolks	3
250 g	coconut, shredded	3⅓ cups
120 g	chocolate, shaved	4 squares
100 g	hazelnuts, finely ground	1 cup
3	egg whites	3
200 g	icing sugar, sifted	2 cups

Decoration:

100 g	icing sugar, sifted	¾ cup
1 pkg	**oetker** vanilla sugar (9 g)	1 pkg

PREHEAT oven to 160°C (325°F). Lightly grease a baking sheet.
IN a mixing bowl, combine egg yolks, coconut, chocolate and hazelnuts. Mix well.

BEAT egg whites to soft peaks. Gradually beat in icing sugar until stiff peaks form. (Peaks should be so stiff that when a knife is inserted, the cut remains visible.)
FOLD beaten egg whites into coconut mixture, gently but thoroughly.

SHAPE mixture into balls the size of a walnut.
MIX together icing sugar and vanilla sugar.
ROLL balls in sugar mixture.
PLACE on prepared baking sheet.
BAKE for 15-20 minutes.

Egg Yolk Rounds

Dotterlaibchen

Recipe No. 794

Ingredients:

10	egg yolks	10	
100 g	icing sugar, sifted	¾ cup	
2 pkgs	**oetker** vanilla sugar (18 g)	2 pkgs	
pinch	salt	pinch	
150 g	all-purpose flour, sifted	1¼ cups	

Filling:

125 mL	red currant jam	½ cup	

Dipping:

1 pkg	**oetker** Chocofix (100 g)	1 pkg	

PREHEAT oven to 230°C (450°F). Grease a baking sheet.
IN a mixing bowl, beat egg yolks, icing sugar, vanilla sugar and salt until fluffy.
SIFT flour over egg yolk mixture. Mix well.

PLACE mixture in a pastry bag fitted with a plain tube.
PIPE walnut size portions onto prepared baking sheet.
BAKE for 5-7 minutes.

REMOVE warm cookies from baking sheet.
COOL completely on wire racks.
SPREAD jam on the underside of half of the cookies.
TOP with remaining cookies.

PREPARE Chocofix according to package directions.
DIP one-quarter of the cookie into the Chocofix.

Lieutenant-Colonel Kisses

Oberstleutnant-Busserln

Recipe No. 795

Ingredients:

150 g	butter, softened	⅔ cup	
280 g	icing sugar, sifted	2⅓ cups	
1 pkg	**oetker** vanilla sugar (9 g)	1 pkg	
150 g	walnuts or hazelnuts, ground	1½ cups	
2 pinches	baking soda	2 pinches	
30 g	cocoa	5 tbsp	
60 g	semi-sweet chocolate, softened	2 squares	

Decoration:

some	almond slivers	some	

LIGHTLY grease a baking sheet.
IN a mixing bowl, combine butter, icing sugar, vanilla sugar, nuts, baking soda, cocoa and chocolate. Mix well.
CHILL for 30 minutes.
PREHEAT oven to 120°C (250°F).
SHAPE mixture into balls the size of a walnut.
PLACE on prepared baking sheet.
DECORATE with sliced almonds.
BAKE for 15-18 minutes.

*H*azelnut Kisses

Haselnußbusserln

Recipe No. 796

Ingredients:

200 g	semi-sweet chocolate	7 squares	
150 g	butter	⅔ cup	
150 g	icing sugar, sifted	1½ cups	
1 pkg	**oetker** vanilla sugar (9 g)	1 pkg	
200 g	hazelnuts, ground	2 cups	

LIGHTLY grease a baking sheet.
IN a double boiler, heat chocolate until melted.
IN a mixing bowl, beat butter, icing sugar and vanilla sugar until fluffy.
STIR in melted chocolate.
FOLD in hazelnuts, gently but thoroughly.
LET dough rest for 1 hour.

PREHEAT oven to 150°C (300°F).
SHAPE mixture into 1 cm (⅜") balls.
PLACE on prepared baking sheet.
BAKE for 25-30 minutes.

Pastry Bites

Essigwürferln

Recipe No. 797

Dough:

250 g	all-purpose flour	1¾ cups	
½ pkg	**oetker** baking powder (7 g)	½ pkg	
5 drops	**oetker** lemon flavouring concentrate	5 drops	
90 mL	water	6 tbsp	
45 mL	vinegar	3 tbsp	
220 g	cold butter	1 cup	

Decoration:

100 g	icing sugar, sifted	¾ cup	
1 pkg	**oetker** vanilla sugar (9 g)	1 pkg	
some	cinnamon	some	

Dough:

LIGHTLY grease a baking sheet.

SIFT flour and baking powder onto a working surface.

MAKE a well in the centre. Put flavouring concentrate, water and vinegar in the well.

CUT butter in small pieces over the ingredients in the well.

COVER with flour.

STARTING from the centre, work all ingredients into a smooth dough.

CHILL for 30 minutes.

PREHEAT oven to 200°C (400°F).

ROLL out dough to a ½ cm (¼") thickness.

USING a knife, cut out 2 cm (1") squares.

(Roll out only as much dough as can be worked. Chill remaining dough until ready to use.)

PLACE squares on prepared baking sheet.

BAKE for 15-20 minutes.

IN a mixing bowl, combine icing sugar, vanilla sugar and cinnamon.

ROLL the warm squares in the sugar mixture.

Chocolate-Cherry Bites

Maraschinokugerln

Recipe No. 798

Ingredients:
Mixture 1:

30	mL	butter	2 tbsp
1		egg yolk, cooked	1
1	pkg	**oetker** vanilla sugar (9 g)	1 pkg
30	mL	cherry liqueur	2 tbsp

Mixture 2:

1		egg white	1
100	g	sugar	½ cup
100	g	chocolate, shaved	3½ squares
50	g	almonds, ground	½ cup
10	mL	rum	2 tsp

Decoration:
chocolate sprinkles

Mixture 1:

IN a mixing bowl, beat butter until light and fluffy.
ADD egg yolk, vanilla sugar and cherry liqueur. Mix well.
CHILL mixture.

Mixture 2:

IN another bowl, combine egg white, sugar, chocolate, almonds and rum. Mix well.
CHILL for 30 minutes.

SHAPE mixture 2 into balls the size of a walnut. Flatten. Fill with mixture 1. Form balls. ROLL in chocolate sprinkles.

Wedding Delights

Hochzeitskrapferln

Recipe No. 799

Dough:

250 g	all-purpose flour	1¾	cups
100 g	icing sugar, sifted	¾	cup
1 pkg	**oetker** vanilla sugar (9 g)	1	pkg
80 g	semi-sweet chocolate, shaved	3	squares
100 g	walnuts or hazelnuts, ground	1	cup
220 g	cold butter	1	cup

Filling:

30 mL	milk	2	tbsp
250 g	sugar	1¼	cups
1 pkg	**oetker** vanilla sugar (9 g)	1	pkg
30 mL	butter	2	tbsp
80 g	semi-sweet chocolate, softened	3	squares
100 g	walnuts or hazelnuts, ground	1	cup
15 mL	rum	1	tbsp

Brushing:

	some apricot jam	some

Glaze:

1 pkg	**oetker** Chocofix (100 g)	1 pkg

Decoration:

	some gold or silver sugar pearls	some

Dough:
LIGHTLY grease a baking sheet.
SIFT flour onto a working surface.
MAKE a well in the centre. Put icing sugar, vanilla sugar, chocolate and nuts in the well.
CUT butter in small pieces over the ingredients in the well.
COVER with flour.
STARTING from the centre, work all ingredients into a smooth dough.
CHILL for 30 minutes.
PREHEAT oven to 180°C (350°F).
ROLL out dough thinly.
USING a round cookie cutter, cut out slices 3-4 cm (1-1½") in diameter.
PLACE slices on prepared baking sheet.
BAKE for approximately 10 minutes.
COOL completely.

Filling:
IN a mixing bowl, beat milk, sugar and vanilla sugar until fluffy.
ADD butter, chocolate, nuts and rum. Mix well.
SPREAD jam over the surface of each cookie.
SPOON filling over jam. Shape into small domes.

Glaze:
PREPARE Chocofix according to package directions.
GLAZE cookies.
DECORATE with sugar pearls.

*B*utter Slices

Innviertler Butterstangerln

Recipe No. 800

Dough:

250 g	all-purpose flour	1¾	cups
2	egg yolks	2	
30 mL	sour cream	2	tbsp
15 mL	vinegar	1	tbsp
220 g	cold butter or margarine	1	cup

Topping:

2	egg whites	2	
250 g	icing sugar, sifted	2	cups
1 pkg	**oetker** vanilla sugar (9 g)	1	pkg

Dough:
LIGHTLY grease a baking sheet.
SIFT flour onto a working surface.
MAKE a well in the centre. Put egg yolks, sour cream and vinegar in the well.
CUT butter in small pieces over ingredients in the well.
COVER with flour.
STARTING from the centre, work all ingredients into a smooth dough.
CHILL overnight.

BEAT egg whites to soft peaks.
GRADUALLY beat in icing sugar and vanilla sugar until stiff peaks form. (Peaks should be so stiff that when a knife is inserted, the cut remains visible.)

PREHEAT oven to 180°C (350°F).
ROLL out dough thinly.
USING a knife, cut dough into 5 cm (2") slices.
SPREAD beaten egg white mixture evenly over the dough slices.

PLACE on prepared baking sheet.
BAKE for approximately 15 minutes.

Marzipan Treats

Kieler Marzipangebäck

Recipe No. 801

Ingredients:

250	g	marzipan	9 oz
150	g	icing sugar, sifted	1⅓ cups
45	mL	whipping cream	3 tbsp
3		egg whites	3
50	g	butter, melted	¼ cup
90	g	all-purpose flour, sifted	⅔ cup

Sprinkling:

50	g	almond slivers, lightly toasted	⅓ cup

Filling:

200	g	nougat, softened	7 oz

PREHEAT oven to 180°C (350°F). Lightly grease a baking sheet.
IN a mixing bowl, combine marzipan, icing sugar, whipping cream and egg whites.
BEAT until marzipan mixture is lump-free.
STIR in butter.
SLOWLY add flour to the marzipan mixture.
CONTINUE stirring until entire mixture is smooth.

DROP marzipan mixture by the teaspoon onto prepared baking sheet. Flatten.
SPRINKLE half of the cookies with almond slivers.
BAKE for 10-15 minutes.

IN a double boiler, soften nougat until it becomes spreadable.
SPREAD nougat on the underside of the plain marzipan cookies. Top with almond covered cookies.

Suggestion: For best results, store cookies one week.

*H*orseshoes

Klosterkipferln

Recipe No. 802

Dough:

210 g	all-purpose flour	1⅔ cups
2	egg yolks	2
50 g	sugar	¼ cup
1 pkg	**oetker** vanilla sugar (9 g)	1 pkg
150 g	almonds or hazelnuts, ground	1¾ cups
100 g	milk chocolate, shaved	3½ squares
150 g	butter	⅔ cup

Dipping:

1 pkg	**oetker** Chocofix (100 g)	1 pkg
50 g	pistachio nuts, chopped	⅓ cup

Dough:

PREHEAT oven to 120°C (250°F).
SIFT flour onto a working surface.
MAKE a well in the centre.
PUT egg yolks, sugar, vanilla sugar, nuts and chocolate in the well.
CUT cold butter in small pieces over the ingredients in the well.
COVER with flour.
STARTING from the centre, work all ingredients into a smooth dough.

SHAPE dough into rolls the size of a pencil.
CUT into 5 cm (2") long pieces.
SHAPE into crescents.
PLACE on baking sheet.
BAKE for 25 minutes.
COOL completely.

Dipping:

PREPARE Chocofix according to package directions.
DIP the ends of each crescent into the Chocofix.
DIP ends into chopped nuts before Chocofix sets.

*S*ea Shells

Sandmuscheln

Recipe No. 803

Ingredients:

100 g	marzipan	3½ oz	
300 g	butter or margarine, softened	1⅓ cups	
130 g	icing sugar, sifted	1 cup	
1 pkg	**oetker** vanilla sugar (9 g)	1 pkg	
pinch	salt	pinch	
2	egg whites	2	
350 g	all-purpose flour	2½ cups	

Filling:

some apricot jam   some

Decoration:

1 pkg   **oetker** Chocofix (100 g)   1 pkg

PREHEAT oven to 180°C (350°F). Lightly grease a baking sheet.

IN a mixing bowl, beat marzipan, butter or margarine, icing sugar, vanilla sugar and salt until fluffy.

GRADUALLY beat in egg whites.

SIFT flour over butter mixture. Using a wooden spoon, stir mixture quickly and only until all the flour has been absorbed by the butter mixture. (Stirring too long makes the mixture glutenous and thus difficult to squeeze out of the pastry bag.)

PLACE mixture in a pastry bag fitted with a star tube.

PIPE shell shapes on prepared baking sheet.

BAKE for 8-10 minutes.

COOL completely.

SPREAD jam on the underside of half the shells.

TOP with remaining shells.

PREPARE Chocofix according to package directions.

GLAZE cookies as desired.

Orange Rounds

Orangentaler

Recipe No. 804

Dough:

180 mL	honey	¾ cup	
50 g	sugar	¼ cup	
½ pkg	**oetker** vanilla sugar (4.5 g)	½ pkg	
30 mL	water	2 tbsp	
180 g	rye flour	1⅔ cups	
180 g	wholewheat flour	1½ cups	
5 mL	**oetker** baking powder	1 tsp	
10 mL	cinnamon	2 tsp	
5 mL	cloves, ground	1 tsp	
pinch	cardamon	pinch	
pinch	allspice	pinch	
1	egg yolk	1	

Filling:

150 mL	orange marmalade	⅔ cup	
1 shot	orange liqueur	1 shot	

Glaze:

1 pkg	**oetker** Chocofix (100 g)	1 pkg	

Decoration:

some	candied orange peel,	
some		
	chopped	

Dough:

LIGHTLY grease a baking sheet.
IN a saucepan, combine honey, sugar, vanilla sugar and water.
HEAT mixture, stirring constantly, until sugar has dissolved.
REMOVE from heat. Cool completely.
MIX together flour and baking powder.
SIFT over honey mixture.
ADD spices. Mix well.

ADD egg yolk to honey mixture.
WORK mixture into a smooth dough.
WRAP dough in aluminum foil.
CHILL overnight.

PREHEAT oven to 180°C (350°F).
ON a lightly floured surface, roll out dough to an 8 mm (⅛") thickness.
USING a round cookie cutter, cut out slices 4 - 5 cm (1½ - 2") in diameter.
PLACE slices on prepared baking sheet.
BAKE for 10-12 minutes.

Filling:

MIX together marmalade and liqueur.
SPREAD jam mixture on the underside of one-half of the slices. Sandwich together.

Glaze:

PREPARE Chocofix according to package directions.
GLAZE cookies.
BEFORE glaze has set completely, decorate cookies with candied orange peel.

Suggestion: These cookies will become soft only after a few days of storage.

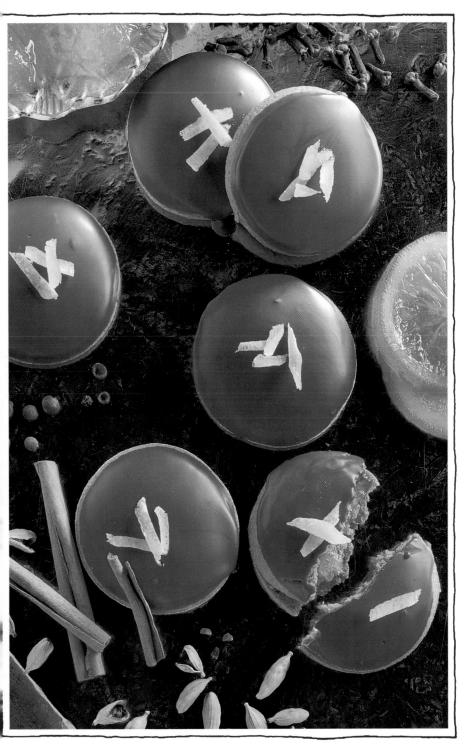

Crackling Cookies

Grammelbäckerei

Recipe No. 805

Dough:

400 g	all-purpose flour	3	cups
1 pkg	**oetker** baking powder (14 g)	1	pkg
200 g	all-vegetable shortening	1	cup
2	eggs	2	
150 g	sugar	⅔	cup
45 mL	milk	3	tbsp
pinch	salt		pinch
5 drops	**oetker** lemon flavouring concentrate	5	drops
2 mL	ground cloves	½	tsp
2 mL	cinnamon	½	tsp
	juice of ½ lemon		

Filling:

250 mL	red currant jam	1	cup

Sprinkling:

some	icing sugar		some
1 pkg	**oetker** vanilla sugar (9 g)	1	pkg

Dough:

LINE a baking sheet with parchment paper.
MIX together flour and baking powder. Sift onto a working surface.
MAKE a well in the centre.
PUT shortening, eggs, sugar, milk, salt, flavouring concentrate, spices and lemon juice in the well.
COVER with flour.
STARTING from the centre, work all ingredients into a smooth dough.
CHILL for 30 minutes.

PREHEAT oven to 180°C (350°F).
ROLL out dough to a 3-4 mm (⅛") thickness.
USING a variety of cookie cutters, cut out shapes.
PLACE shapes on prepared baking sheet.
BAKE on middle oven rack for 12 minutes.
COOL completely.

SPREAD jam on the underside of one-half of the cookies.
TOP with remaining cookies.
MIX together icing sugar and vanilla sugar.
DECORATE cookies with sugar mixture.

Tender Hearts

Feine Kekse

Recipe No. 806

Dough:

500 g	all-purpose flour	3½ cups	
½ pkg	**oetker** baking powder (7 g)	½ pkg	
4	egg yolks	4	
250 g	icing sugar, sifted	2 cups	
1 pkg	**oetker** vanilla sugar (9 g)	1 pkg	
15-30 mL	whipping cream grated peel of 1 lemon OR	1-2 tbsp	
5 drops	**oetker** lemon flavouring concentrate	5 drops	
375 g	cold butter	1⅔ cups	

Dough:

PREHEAT oven to 180°C (350°F).

SIFT flour and baking powder onto a working surface.

MAKE a well in the centre.

PUT egg yolks, icing sugar, vanilla sugar, whipping cream and lemon peel or flavouring concentrate in the well.

CUT butter in small pieces over the ingredients in the well.

COVER with flour.

STARTING from the centre, work all ingredients into a smooth dough.

ON a lightly floured surface, roll dough 3 mm (⅛") thick.

USING a heart-shaped cookie cutter, cut out shapes.

PLACE shapes on baking sheet.

BAKE on upper oven rack for 12-15 minutes.

Suggestion: *Cookies can be filled with jam or glazed with Chocofix.*

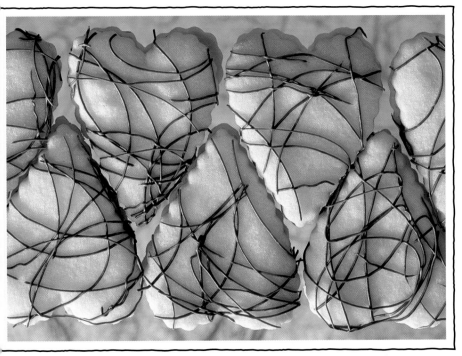

Apricot Pockets

Mostkekse

Recipe No. 807

Dough:

250 g	all-purpose flour	1¾ cups
½ pkg	**oetker** baking powder (7 g)	½ pkg
90 mL	sweet wine or fruit juice	6 tbsp
220 g	cold butter or margarine	1 cup

Brushing:

some	egg white, lightly beaten	some

Filling:

apricot jam

Dusting:

100 g	icing sugar, sifted	¾ cup
1 pkg	**oetker** vanilla sugar (9 g)	1 pkg

Dough:

SIFT flour and baking powder onto a working surface.

MAKE a well in the centre.

PUT wine or fruit juice in the well.

CUT butter or margarine in small pieces over the ingredients in the well.

COVER with flour.

STARTING from the centre, work all ingredients into a smooth dough.

CHILL for 30 minutes.

PREHEAT oven to 180°C (350°F).

ROLL out dough 3 mm (⅛") thick.

USING a round cookie cutter, cut out slices 6 cm (2¼") in diameter.

BRUSH outer edge of each slice with beaten egg white.

PLACE a small amount of jam in the centre of each circle.

FOLD each circle over in the shape of a half moon. Press edges lightly together.

PLACE cookies on baking sheet.

BAKE for 12-15 minutes.

MIX together icing sugar and vanilla sugar.

DUST warm pastry with the sugar mixture.

Chocolate Spheres

Notarkugerln

Recipe No. 808

Ingredients:
Mixture 1:

30 mL	butter, softened	2 tbsp
30 mL	icing sugar, sifted	2 tbsp
2	cooked egg yolks, strained	2
3 drops	**oetker** rum flavouring concentrate	3 drops

Mixture 2:

2	egg whites	2
200 g	chocolate, shaved	7 squares
200 g	icing sugar, sifted	2 cups
100 g	almonds, ground	1 cup
60 mL	rum	4 tbsp

Decoration:

100 g	chocolate, shaved	3-4 squares

Mixture 1:

IN a mixing bowl, combine butter, icing sugar, egg yolks and flavouring concentrate. Stir well.
SHAPE mixture into small balls.
CHILL.

Mixture 2:

IN another mixing bowl, beat egg whites, chocolate, icing sugar, almonds and rum until smooth.

FORM mixture 2 into balls. Flatten.
PLACE mixture 1 balls in centre of mixture 2.
SHAPE into balls.
ROLL in shaved chocolate.
PLACE in small confectionary cups.
CHILL.

Suggestion: *Moisten hands before shaping mixture into balls.*

*P*laying Cards

Spielkartenbäckerei (aus Urgroßmutters Backstube)

Recipe No. 809

Dough:

210 g	all-purpose flour	1⅔ cups
	pinch	**oetker** baking powder	pinch
150 g	icing sugar, sifted	1⅓ cups
1 pkg	**oetker** vanilla sugar (9 g)	1 pkg
	pinch	cloves, ground	pinch
	grated peel of 1 lemon	
1	egg yolk	1
150 g	cold butter	⅔ cup

Brushing:

| 1 | egg white, lightly beaten | 1 |

Filling:

| 150 mL | red currant jam | ⅔ cup |

Dusting:

| some | icing sugar, sifted | some |

Dough:

PREHEAT oven to 160°C (325°F).
SIFT flour and baking powder onto a working surface.
MAKE a well in the centre. Put icing sugar, vanilla sugar, cloves, lemon peel and egg yolk in the well.
CUT butter in small pieces over ingredients in the well. Cover with flour.
STARTING from the centre, work all ingredients into a smooth dough.
CHILL for one hour.

ROLL out dough thinly.
USING a cookie cutter or knife, cut out 8 x 5 cm (3 x 2") rectangles.
USING small cookie cutters in the shape of hearts, diamonds, spades and crosses, cut out shapes from the centre of half the rectangles.

BRUSH rectangles with egg white.
PLACE on baking sheet.
BAKE for 10-12 minutes.

AFTER baking, brush the underside of the solid rectangles with jam.
TOP with rectangles with cut-outs.
DUST with icing sugar.

Lace Cookies

Spitzenkekse

Recipe No. 810

Ingredients:

175 g	rolled oats	2 cups
200 g	butter or margarine, melted	1 cup
275 g	brown sugar	2 cups
1 pkg	**oetker** vanilla sugar (9 g)	1 pkg
1	egg	1
45 mL	all-purpose flour	3 tbsp
pinch	salt	pinch
15 mL	honey	1 tbsp

IN a mixing bowl, combine rolled oats, butter or margarine, brown sugar and vanilla sugar.
MIX well.
PREHEAT oven to 220°C (425°F).
IN another mixing bowl, beat egg until fluffy.
SIFT flour and salt over the beaten egg.
STIR in honey.
FOLD into rolled oats mixture, gently but thoroughly.

DROP mixture from a teaspoon, 6 cm (2½") apart, onto baking sheet.
BAKE for 3-5 minutes.
COOL completely.

CAREFULLY remove cookies from baking sheet.

*S*nowballs

Schneebällchen

Recipe No. 811

Dough:

80	g	all-purpose flour	½ cup
5	mL	**oetker** baking powder	1 tsp
50	mL	bread crumbs	¼ cup
120	g	chocolate, shaved	4 squares
350	g	walnuts or hazelnuts, ground	3½ cups
3		eggs	3
250	g	icing sugar, sifted	2 cups
1	pkg	**oetker** vanilla sugar (9 g)	1 pkg
5	mL	rum	1 tsp
		OR	
3	drops	**oetker** rum flavouring concentrate	3 drops

Decoration:

100	g	icing sugar, sifted	¾ cup
1	pkg	**oetker** vanilla sugar (9 g)	1 pkg

Dough:

PREHEAT oven to 150°C (300°F).

SIFT flour and baking powder onto a working surface.

ADD bread crumbs, chocolate, nuts, eggs, icing sugar, vanilla sugar and rum or flavouring concentrate.

WORK into a smooth dough.

SHAPE dough into a roll, 5 cm (2") in diameter.

CUT off pieces, 1 cm (⅜") in length.

SHAPE each piece into a ball.

IN another bowl, mix together icing sugar and vanilla sugar.

ROLL each ball in the sugar mixture.

PLACE balls on baking sheet.

BAKE for 18-20 minutes.

Snickerdoodles

Snickerdoodles

Recipe No. 812

1	egg	1
30 mL	butter or margarine	2 tbsp
50 g	brown sugar	½ cup
90 g	all-purpose flour	⅔ cup
5 mL	**oetker** baking powder	1 tsp
5 mL	cinnamon	1 tsp
pinch	cloves, ground	pinch
pinch	nutmeg, ground	pinch
60 mL	whisky	4 tbsp
175 g	raisins or figs, chopped	1⅓ cups
200 g	walnuts, finely chopped	1¾ cups
200 g	candied cherries, finely chopped	1⅓ cups

Mixture:

PREHEAT oven to 180°C (350°F). Lightly grease a baking sheet.
IN a mixing bowl, beat egg, butter or margarine and brown sugar until fluffy.
IN another bowl, mix together flour and baking powder.
SIFT over egg mixture.
ADD spices and whisky.
MIX well.
ADD raisins, walnuts and cherries. Stir thoroughly.

DROP mixture from a teaspoon onto prepared baking sheet.
BAKE for 12-15 minutes.

Mozart Slices

Mozartscheiben

Recipe No. 813

Dough:

250 g	all-purpose flour	1¾ cups
1	egg	1
100 g	sugar	½ cup
100 g	hazelnuts, ground	1 cup
110 g	cold butter	½ cup

Filling:

110 g	butter	½ cup
100 g	icing sugar, sifted	¾ cup
1 pkg	**oetker** vanilla sugar (9 g)	1 pkg
100 g	nuts, ground	1 cup
15 mL	rum	1 tbsp

Decoration:

| some | walnut halves | some |
| some | icing sugar, sifted | some |

Dough:

SIFT flour onto a working surface.
MAKE a well in the centre. Put egg, sugar and hazelnuts in the well.
CUT butter in small pieces over the ingredients in the well.
COVER with flour.
STARTING from the centre, work all ingredients into a smooth dough.
CHILL for 30 minutes.

Filling:

IN a mixing bowl, beat butter until fluffy.
GRADUALLY beat in icing sugar, vanilla sugar, nuts and rum. Mix well. Chill.
PLACE 30-45 mL (2-3 tbsp) of filling in a pastry bag fitted with a star tube. Reserve.

ROLL out dough thinly.
USING a small round cookie cutter with scalloped edges, cut out slices.
PLACE slices on baking sheet.
PLACE sheet on middle oven rack in <u>cold</u> oven.
BAKE in a 190°C (375°F) oven for 8-10 minutes.

SPREAD filling on the underside of half of the cookies. Cover with remaining cookies.
DECORATE each cookie with reserved filling and walnut halves.
DUST with icing sugar.

Bread & Pastry

Sunflower Bread

Dinkel-SonnenblumenBrot

Recipe No. 814

Dough:

500 g	all-purpose flour	3½ cups
250 g	rye flour	2½ cups
2 pkgs	**oetker** instant dry yeast (14 g)	2 pkgs
10 mL	salt	2 tsp
5 mL	ground caraway	1 tsp
5 mL	ground fennel	1 tsp
400 mL	lukewarm water	1⅔ cups
250 g	quark	1 cup
100 g	sunflower seeds	⅔ cup

Brushing:

some	lukewarm milk	some

Sprinkling:

50 g	sunflower seeds	⅓ cup

Dough:

LIGHTLY grease a baking sheet.

IN a mixing bowl, mix together flour and yeast.

MAKE a well in the centre. Put salt, spices, water and quark in the well.

KNEAD dough with an electric mixer fitted with dough hooks on high speed until dough is smooth, blistery and no longer sticky.

COVER. Let rest in a warm place until doubled in size.

PUNCH down dough.

KNEAD sunflower seeds into the dough.

DIVIDE dough in two. Shape into loaves.

PLACE on prepared baking sheet.

COVER. Let rest in a warm place until doubled in size.

PREHEAT oven to 200°C (400°F).

BRUSH loaves with milk. Sprinkle with sunflower seeds.

BAKE for 60 minutes. After 10 minutes of baking, place a dish of hot water in the oven to prevent the bread from drying out.

Beer Buns

Bierweckerln

Recipe No. 815

Dough:

600 g	all-purpose flour	4½	cups
2 pkgs	**oetker** instant dry yeast (14 g)	2	pkgs
50 mL	sugar	¼	cup
125 mL	warm water	½	cup
250 mL	light beer, room temperature	1	cup
10 mL	salt	2	tsp
90 mL	butter, softened	6	tbsp

Dough:

SIFT flour into a large, warm mixing bowl.

ADD yeast, sugar, warm water, beer, salt and butter.

BEAT with an electric mixer, with dough hook attachments, until dough is smooth.

TURN dough onto floured surface.

KNEAD 5-10 minutes or until dough becomes smooth, elastic and no longer sticky. (Add more flour if necessary.)

PLACE dough in lightly greased bowl. Grease top of dough. Cover with a damp cloth.

LET rise in a warm place until doubled in size.

PUNCH down. Cover and let rest 10 minutes.

SHAPE dough into rolls, as desired.

COVER and let rise in a warm place until doubled in size (30-40 minutes).

PREHEAT oven to 190°C (375°F).

BAKE for 15-18 minutes. Brush with unsalted butter or margarine, if desired.

COOL on wire racks.

Suggestion: *Before baking, buns can be sprinkled with grated cheese or sesame seeds.*

Multi-Grain Bread

Vielkornbrot

Recipe No. 816

Dough:

70 g	flax seed, ground	½	cup
50 g	rolled oats	½	cup
60 g	sunflower seeds, ground	½	cup
150 g	all purpose flour	1	cup
250 g	wholewheat flour	2	cups
1 pkg	**oetker** instant dry yeast (7 g)	1	pkg
5 mL	salt	1	tsp
30 mL	sugar	2	tbsp
15 mL	vegetable oil	1	tbsp
300 mL	lukewarm water	1⅓	cups

Dough:

GREASE a 23 x 13 x 7 cm (9 x 5 x 3") loaf pan.

IN a mixing bowl, combine flax seed, rolled oats, sunflower seeds, flour, yeast, salt and sugar.

IN another bowl, mix together vegetable oil and water. Add to dry ingredients.

KNEAD mixture by hand 100 times.

SET dough in a lightly greased bowl. Cover and let rest in a warm place until doubled in size.

KNEAD dough once more.

TURN into prepared pan. Let rest in a warm place until almost doubled in size.

PREHEAT oven to 200°C (400°F).

MAKE a lengthwise cut along the surface of the dough.

BAKE on middle oven rack for 60-70 minutes.

*P*otato Bread

*K*artoffelbrot

Recipe No. 817

Dough:

2 medium	potatoes, parboiled, grated	2 medium
500 g	all-purpose flour	3½ cups
1 pkg	**oetker** instant dry yeast (7 g)	1 pkg
250 mL	milk	1 cup
2	eggs	2
2 mL	salt	½ tsp
60 g	sugar	¼ cup
60 g	butter or margarine, melted	⅓ cup

Brushing:

30 mL	butter, melted	2 tbsp

Dough:

LINE a baking sheet with parchment paper.
PARBOIL potatoes. Cool completely. Grate.
SIFT flour into a mixing bowl.
ADD yeast. Mix well.
BEAT milk and eggs.
MAKE a well in the centre. Put beaten egg mixture, salt, sugar, butter or margarine and potatoes in the well.
KNEAD dough with an electric mixer fitted with dough hooks on high speed until dough is smooth, blistery and no longer sticky.
COVER. Let rest in a warm place until doubled in size.

KNEAD dough.
DIVIDE into two equal parts.
SHAPE into loaves.
PLACE on prepared baking sheet.
COVER. Let rest in a warm place for 30 minutes.
PREHEAT oven to 180°C (350°F).
BAKE for 30 minutes.
AFTER baking, brush immediately with melted butter.

Poppy Seed Plum Pockets

Ab-Druckte

Recipe No. 818

Dough:

9-10 medium	potatoes, boiled, strained	9-10 medium
550 g	all-purpose flour, sifted	4 cups
1 pkg	**oetker** baking powder (14 g)	1 pkg
220 g	cold butter or margarine	1 cup
2	eggs	2
200 g	icing sugar, sifted	2 cups
1 pkg	**oetker** vanilla sugar (9 g)	1 pkg
	grated peel of 1 lemon OR	
½ btl	**oetker** lemon flavouring concentrate	½ btl

Filling:

250 mL	milk	1 cup
150 g	sugar	¾ cup
1 pkg	**oetker** vanilla sugar (9 g)	1 pkg
30 mL	honey	2 tbsp
350 g	poppy seeds, ground	3⅓ cups
125 mL	plum jam	½ cup
some	rum	some
some	cinnamon	some
	grated peel of 1 lemon OR	
½ btl	**oetker** lemon flavouring concentrate	½ btl

Brushing:

1	egg	1
some	milk	some

Dough:

BOIL and prepare potatoes one day in advance. Cool completely.

IN a mixing bowl, combine flour and baking powder.
ADD butter or margarine. Mix well.
ADD potatoes, eggs, icing sugar, vanilla sugar and lemon peel or flavouring concentrate.
WORK all ingredients into a smooth dough.

Filling:

IN a saucepan, bring milk, sugar and vanilla sugar to a boil.
STIRRING constantly, add honey and poppy seeds.
STIR in plum jam, rum, cinnamon and lemon peel or flavouring concentrate.
REMOVE from heat. Cool completely.
PREHEAT oven to 180°C (350°F).

DIVIDE dough into three equal parts.
ROLL out each portion thinly to form 30 x 40 cm (12 x 16") rectangles.
SPREAD filling mixture evenly over each dough rectangle.
ROLL up dough at both ends so that the rolls meet in the centre.
USING the handle of a wooden spoon, separate dough into 5 cm (2") pieces.

LIGHTLY beat egg and milk.
BRUSH pastry with egg mixture.
USING a fork, prick the surface of each piece several times.
PLACE on baking sheet.
BAKE for 30 minutes.

Desserts

*F*ruit Surprise

Früchteterrine

Recipe No. 819

Ingredients:

250 g	quark or cream cheese	1 cup
	juice of ½ lemon	
	juice of ½ orange	
30-45 mL	honey	2-3 tbsp
125 mL	yogurt	½ cup
125 mL	sour cream	½ cup
	some orange liqueur	some
1 pkg	**oetker** vanilla sugar (9 g)	1 pkg
1 pkg	gelatin (dissolved in 45 mL/3 tbsp of boiling water)	1 pkg
250 mL	whipping cream	1 cup

Filling:

16	lady fingers	16
500 mL	strawberries	2 cups

Decoration:

	assorted fruits

LINE a 23 x 13 x 7 cm (9 x 5 x 3") loaf pan
with aluminum foil.
IN a mixing bowl, combine quark or cream
cheese, lemon and orange juice and honey.
STIR until creamy.
FOLD yogurt and sour cream into the cheese
mixture.
STIR in liqueur and vanilla sugar.
FOLD gelatin into the cheese mixture.
BEAT whipping cream to stiff peaks.
FOLD whipped cream into cheese mixture,
gently but thoroughly.
TURN one-quarter of the cheese mixture into
the prepared pan.
TOP with lady fingers.
COVER with one-quarter of the cheese mixture.
TOP evenly with lady fingers.
COVER with one-quarter of the cheese mixture.
TOP with fruit.
PLACE lady fingers over top of the fruit.
COVER with remaining quark mixture.
CHILL overnight.
TURN onto a serving platter.
REMOVE aluminum foil.
CUT into pieces. Decorate with fruit.

Cream of Wheat & Quark Fruit Soufflé

Grieß-Topfen-Früchteauflauf

Recipe No. 820

Ingredients:

500 mL	milk	2	cups
pinch	salt		pinch
55 g	butter	¼	cup
150 g	cream of wheat	¾	cup
3	egg yolks	3	
3	egg whites	3	
100 g	icing sugar, sifted	¾	cup
1 pkg	**oetker** vanilla sugar (9 g)	1	pkg
250 g	quark or cream cheese, softened	1	cup

Filling:

500 mL	fruits in season	2	cups

PREHEAT oven to 160°C (325°F). Grease a 23 x 13 x 7 cm (9 x 5 x 3") loaf pan.
IN a saucepan, bring milk and salt to a boil.
ADD butter. Stir until melted.
ADD cream of wheat. Bring to a quick boil.
REMOVE from heat. Let cool.
WHISK egg yolks. Fold into cream of wheat mixture.

IN a mixing bowl, beat egg whites to stiff peaks. Gradually beat in icing sugar and vanilla sugar.
SET aside one-third of the beaten egg white mixture.
FOLD remaining egg white mixture and quark or cream cheese into cream of wheat mixture, gently but thoroughly.

TURN one-half of the mixture into prepared pan.
SMOOTH surface with a knife.
TOP with fruit.
POUR remaining mixture over the fruit.
SPREAD reserved egg white mixture evenly over the surface.
BAKE for 40-50 minutes.

Special Dumplings

Somloer Nockerl (ungarische Spezialität)

Recipe No. 821

Batter:			
8	egg yolks	8	
80 g	icing sugar, sifted (first amount)	¾ cup	
1 pkg	**oetker** vanilla sugar (9 g)	1 pkg	
8	egg whites	8	
80 g	icing sugar, sifted (second amount)	¾ cup	
140 g	all-purpose flour	1¼ cups	
20 g	cocoa, sifted	¼ cup	
Sprinkling:			
125 mL	water	½ cup	
100 g	sugar	½ cup	
60 mL	rum	4 tbsp	
Filling:			
750 mL	milk	3 cups	
4	egg yolks	4	
200 g	icing sugar, sifted	1¾ cups	
2 pkgs	**oetker** vanilla sugar (18 g)	2 pkgs	
80 g	all-purpose flour	⅔ cup	
Chocolate Sauce:			
125 mL	water	½ cup	
100 g	sugar	½ cup	
50 g	cocoa	½ cup	
125 mL	rum	½ cup	
Sprinkling:			
150 g	raisins	1 cup	
150 g	almonds, ground	1¾ cups	

Batter:

PREHEAT oven to 200°C (400°F). Line a 40 x 25 x 2 cm (15½ x 10½ x ¾") jelly roll pan with parchment paper.
IN a mixing bowl, combine egg yolks, icing sugar (first amount) and vanilla sugar. Beat until thick and fluffy.
IN another bowl, beat egg whites to stiff peaks. Gradually beat in icing sugar (second amount).
FOLD beaten egg whites and flour into the egg yolk mixture, gently but thoroughly.
SPREAD one-half of the batter 1 cm (⅜") thick into prepared pan (light batter).
BAKE 12 minutes.
AFTER baking, turn cake onto a tea towel sprinkled generously with icing sugar.
BRUSH paper with cold water. Remove carefully but quickly.

ADD cocoa to remaining batter (dark batter).
MIX well.
SPREAD batter into prepared pan.
BAKE as instructed above.

Sprinkling:

IN a saucepan, combine water and sugar.
BRING to a boil. Remove from heat.
COOL completely.
STIR in rum.

Filling:

IN another saucepan, combine milk, egg yolks, icing sugar, vanilla sugar and flour.
STIR until smooth.
COOK until mixture has thickened. Remove from heat. Cool, stirring occasionally.

Chocolate Sauce:

IN a saucepan, combine water, sugar and cocoa. Bring to a boil. Remove from heat.
COOL completely.
STIR in rum.

SET aside two baking dishes, 30 x 19 cm (12 x 7½") in size.
DIVIDE each cake into two.
PLACE one-half of the light cake into each baking dish.
SPRINKLE surface of cake with rum mixture.
SPREAD a portion of the filling evenly over the cake.
SPRINKLE with nuts and raisins.
TOP with one-half of the dark cake.
SPRINKLE surface with rum mixture.
SPREAD filling thinly over cake.
SPRINKLE with nuts and raisins.
CHILL for two to three hours.

USING a spoon, scoop out two portions per serving plate.
DECORATE with chocolate sauce.

*A*pricot Squares

Göttweiger Marillennockerln

Recipe No. 822

Batter:

3	egg yolks	3
40 g	icing sugar, sifted	⅓ cup
1 pkg	**oetker** vanilla sugar (9 g)	1 pkg
3 drops	**oetker** lemon flavouring concentrate	3 drops
3	egg whites	3
50 g	sugar	¼ cup
90 g	all-purpose flour	⅔ cup

Topping:

20	apricot halves	20
some	apricot liqueur	some

Chocolate Sauce:

125 mL	whipping cream	½ cup
50 g	icing sugar, sifted	½ cup
1 pkg	**oetker** vanilla sugar (9 g)	1 pkg
150 g	milk chocolate	5 squares

Topping:

3	egg whites	3
30 mL	sugar	2 tbsp
½ pkg	**oetker** vanilla sugar (4.5 g)	½ pkg
1	egg yolk	1
25 mL	all-purpose flour	1½ tbsp

Batter:

PREHEAT oven to 200°C (400°F). Line a 40 x 25 x 2 cm (15½ x 10½ x ¾") baking sheet with parchment paper.

IN a mixing bowl, combine egg yolks, icing sugar, vanilla sugar and flavouring concentrate. Beat until fluffy.

IN another bowl, beat egg whites to stiff peaks. Gradually beat in sugar.

FOLD beaten egg whites and flour into the egg yolk mixture, gently but thoroughly.

SPREAD the batter 1 cm (⅜") thick into prepared pan.

BAKE for 8-10 minutes.

AFTER baking, remove cake (with paper attached) from pan. Cool completely.

BRUSH paper with cold water.

REMOVE paper carefully but quickly.

POUR apricot liqueur over apricot halves in a bowl. Cover and chill one hour.

Chocolate Sauce:

IN a saucepan, combine whipping cream, icing sugar, vanilla sugar and chocolate.

BRING to a boil, while stirring constantly.

REMOVE from heat. Cool.

PLACE cake on heat-resistant platter.

TOP with marinated apricot halves.

COVER with chocolate sauce.

Topping:

PREHEAT oven to 190°C (375°F).

IN a mixing bowl, beat egg whites to soft peaks. Gradually beat in sugar and vanilla sugar until stiff peaks form.

IN another bowl, whisk egg yolk.

FOLD whisked egg yolk and flour into egg white mixture, gently but thoroughly.

SPOON out dumpling-size portions of egg mixture. Place on surface of the cake.

BAKE for 10 minutes.

COOL completely. Cut into squares.

Baked Blueberry Yogurt

Geflämmtes Heidelbeerjoghurt

Recipe No. 823

Ingredients:

2	egg yolks	2	
120 g	sugar (first amount)	½	cup
150 g	quark	⅔	cup
700 mL	yogurt	3	cups
400 g	blueberries, fresh or frozen	3½	cups
	juice of ½ lemon		
3	egg whites	3	
150 g	sugar (second amount)	¼	cup
1 pkg	**oetker** vanilla sugar (9 g)	1	pkg

IN a mixing bowl, combine egg yolks, sugar *(first amount), quark and yogurt. Mix well.*
FOLD in blueberries and lemon juice, gently but thoroughly.

TURN mixture into heat-resistant dessert dishes.
CHILL for 2-3 hours.

PREHEAT oven to 220°C (425°F).

IN a mixing bowl, beat egg whites to soft peaks. Gradually beat in sugar (second amount) and vanilla sugar until stiff peaks form. (Peaks should be so stiff that when a knife is inserted, the cut remains visible.)
PLACE beaten egg white mixture in a pastry bag fitted with a star tube.
PIPE mixture on chilled desserts.
BAKE on upper oven rack for 10 minutes.

CHILL before serving.

Red Currant Triangles

M*armeladezipferln*

Recipe No. 824

Dough:

300 g	all-purpose flour	2¼	cups
125 mL	sour cream	½	cup
7 mL	vinegar	1½	tsp
pinch	salt		pinch
220 g	cold butter	1	cup

Filling:

175 mL	red currant jam	¾	cup

Brushing:

1	egg, lightly beaten	1	

Decoration:

150 g	icing sugar, sifted	1⅓	cups
1 pkg	**oetker** vanilla sugar (9 g)	1	pkg

SIFT flour onto a working surface.
MAKE a well in the centre. Put sour cream, vinegar and salt in the well.
CUT butter in small pieces over the ingredients in the well.
COVER with flour.
STARTING from the centre, work ingredients into a smooth dough.
CHILL overnight.
PREHEAT oven to 180°C (350°F).
ROLL out dough thinly.
USING a knife, cut out 5 x 5 cm (2 x 2"

White Dreams

Weißer Traum

Recipe No. 825

Batter:

4	egg yolks	4
60 mL	hot water	4 tbsp
120 g	sugar	½ cup
1 pkg	**oetker** vanilla sugar (9 g)	1 pkg
4	egg whites	4
150 g	all-purpose flour	1¼ cups
	pinch **oetker** baking powder	pinch

Sprinkling:

	some rum	some

Filling:

½ pkg	**oetker** vanilla pudding (21 g)	½ pkg
50 g	sugar	¼ cup
175 mL	milk	¾ cup
125 mL	whipping cream	½ cup
1 pkg	**oetker** Whip it (10 g)	1 pkg

Decoration:

100 g	coconut, shredded	1 cup

Batter:

PREHEAT oven to 190°C (375°F). Line a 40 x 25 x 2 cm (15½ x 10½ x ¾") baking sheet with parchment paper.

IN a mixing bowl, combine egg yolks, water, sugar and vanilla sugar. Beat until fluffy.

IN another bowl, beat egg whites to stiff peaks. (Peaks should be so stiff that when a knife is inserted, the cut remains visible.)

FOLD beaten egg whites into the egg yolk mixture.

MIX together flour and baking powder.

SIFT over egg mixture. Fold in gently but thoroughly.

SPREAD batter 1 cm (⅜") thick in prepared baking sheet.

BAKE for 12 minutes.

AFTER baking, turn cake onto a tea towel sprinkled generously with icing sugar.

BRUSH paper with cold water. Remove paper carefully but quickly. Cool completely.

USING a round cookie cutter, cut out slices 5 - 6 cm (2 - 2¼") in diameter.

SPRINKLE each slice with rum.

Filling:

IN a mixing bowl, combine pudding powder and sugar with 6 tbsp of the pre-measured milk.

IN a saucepan, bring remaining milk to a boil.

REMOVE from heat. Gradually stir in pudding mixture.

BRING mixture to a boil. Remove from heat.

COOL completely.

IN a mixing bowl, beat whipping cream and Whip it to stiff peaks.

FOLD whipped cream mixture into pudding mixture, gently but thoroughly.

SPREAD filling on the underside of half the slices. Cover with remaining slices.

SPREAD remaining filling over surface and sides of slices.

ROLL in shredded coconut.

Recipe Index

The **oetker** *Library of Baking*

Baking is Fun — The ABC's of Baking   This book will guide you through a variety of baking techniques. Learn how to prepare batters, doughs, fillings and glazes. Complete with decorating ideas and helpful hints.

Baking Is Fun — Volume 1 (Recipes No. 1 - 93)   Prepare Traditional European desserts such as Black Forest Cake, Hazelnut Cream Torte and Apple Strudel with the aid of this book.

Baking Is Fun — Volume 2 (Recipes No. 94 - 190)   A unique collection of European baking specialties.

Baking Is Fun — Volume 3 (Recipes No. 191 - 270)   This volume consists of Traditional Holiday recipes for the Christmas season. This volume also contains a special section on recipes for diabetics.

Baking Is Fun — Volume 4 (Recipes No. 271 - 350)   Light Wholesome Baking is the principal theme of Volume 4. Make a soufflé, a specialty bread or a gourmet dessert. There are many recipes to choose from.

Baking Is Fun — Volume 5 (Recipes No. 351 - 433)   This volume contains a rich assortment of tempting yeast recipes.

Baking Is Fun — Volume 6 (Recipes No. 434 - 513)   This volume, entitled "Specialties of the World", takes you on a culinary trip around the world with recipes from Austria to Australia and China to Sicily.

Baking Is Fun — Volume 7 (Recipes No. 514 - 593)   This volume contains many Classic European recipes.

Baking Is Fun — Volume 8 (Recipes No. 594 - 678)   A collection of tantalizing cookie recipes . . . from sweet to savoury. Something for every taste and temptation.

Baking Is Fun — Volume 9 (Recipes No. 679 - 750)   Tempt your palate with a unique variety of enticing dessert recipes prepared with fruit.

Baking Is Fun — Volume 10 (Recipes No. 751 - 825)   This volume contains an assortment of the best recipes from private recipe collections.

To order these books please write to:

oetker Recipe Service
2229 Drew Road
Mississauga, Ontario
L5S 1E5